It's another great book from CGP...

GCSE Additional Science is all about **understanding how science works**. And not only that — understanding it well enough to be able to **question** what you hear on TV and read in the papers.

But don't panic. This book includes all the **science facts** you need to learn, and shows you how they work in the real world. It even includes a **free** Online Edition you can read on your computer or tablet.

How to get your free Online Edition

Just go to **cgpbooks.co.uk/extras** and enter this code...

2149 2949 8373 9355

By the way, this code only works for one person. If somebody else has used this book before you, they might have already claimed the Online Edition.

CGP — still the best! ☺

Our sole aim here at CGP is to produce the highest quality books — carefully written, immaculately presented and dangerously close to being funny.

Then we work our socks off to get them out to you — at the cheapest possible prices.

Contents

Published by CGP

From original material by Richard Parsons.

Editors:
Charlotte Burrows, Katherine Craig, Ben Fletcher, Helena Hayes, Felicity Inkpen,
Rosie McCurrie, Jane Sawers, Sarah Williams.

ISBN: 978 1 84762 762 9

With thanks to Mark A Edwards, Chris Elliss, Mary Falkner, David Hickinson, Sue Hocking
and Dawn Wright for the proofreading.
With thanks to Jan Greenway, Laura Jakubowski and Laura Stoney for the copyright research.

Data used to construct stopping distance diagram on page 77 from the Highway Code. ©
Crown Copyright re-produced under the terms of the Click-Use licence.

Printed by Elanders Ltd, Newcastle upon Tyne.
Clipart from Corel®

The Scientific Process

You need to know a few things about how the world of science works. First up is the <u>scientific process</u> — how a scientist's <u>mad idea</u> turns into a <u>widely accepted theory</u>.

Scientists Come Up with <u>Hypotheses</u> — Then <u>Test</u> Them

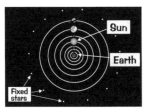

About 500 years ago, we still thought the Solar System looked like this.

1) Scientists try to <u>explain</u> things. Everything.

2) They start by <u>observing</u> something they don't understand — it could be anything, e.g. planets in the sky, a person suffering from an illness, what matter is made of... anything.

3) Then, they come up with a <u>hypothesis</u> — a <u>possible explanation</u> for what they've observed.

4) The next step is to <u>test</u> whether the hypothesis might be <u>right or not</u> — this involves <u>gathering evidence</u> (i.e. <u>data</u> from <u>investigations</u>).

5) The scientist uses the hypothesis to make a <u>prediction</u> — a statement based on the hypothesis that can be <u>tested</u>. They then <u>carry out an investigation</u>.

6) If data from experiments or studies <u>backs up the prediction</u>, you're one step closer to figuring out if the hypothesis is true.

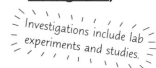
Investigations include lab experiments and studies.

Other Scientists Will <u>Test</u> the Hypothesis Too

1) <u>Other</u> scientists will use the hypothesis to make their <u>own predictions</u>, and carry out their <u>own experiments</u> or studies.

2) They'll also try to <u>reproduce</u> the original investigations to check the results.

3) And if <u>all the experiments</u> in the world back up the hypothesis, then scientists start to think it's <u>true</u>.

4) However, if a scientist somewhere in the world does an experiment that <u>doesn't</u> fit with the hypothesis (and other scientists can <u>reproduce</u> these results), then the hypothesis is in trouble.

5) When this happens, scientists have to come up with a new hypothesis (maybe a <u>modification</u> of the old hypothesis, or maybe a completely <u>new</u> one).

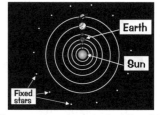
Then we thought it looked like this.

If <u>Evidence</u> Supports a Hypothesis, It's <u>Accepted</u> — <u>for Now</u>

1) If pretty much every scientist in the world believes a hypothesis to be true because experiments back it up, then it usually goes in the <u>textbooks</u> for students to learn.

2) Accepted hypotheses are often referred to as <u>theories</u>.

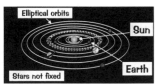
Now we think it's more like this.

3) Our <u>currently accepted</u> theories are the ones that have survived this 'trial by evidence' — they've been tested many, many times over the years and survived (while the less good ones have been ditched).

4) However... they never, <u>never</u> become hard and fast, totally indisputable <u>fact</u>. You can never know... it'd only take <u>one</u> odd, totally inexplicable result, and the hypothesising and testing would start all over again.

You expect me to believe that — then show me the evidence...

If scientists think something is true, they need to produce evidence to convince others — it's all part of <u>testing a hypothesis</u>. One hypothesis might survive these tests, while others won't — it's how things progress. And along the way some hypotheses will be disproved — i.e. shown not to be true.

Your Data's Got To be Good

Evidence is the key to science — but not all evidence is equally good.
The way evidence is <u>gathered</u> can have a big effect on how <u>trustworthy</u> it is...

Lab Experiments and Studies Are Better Than Rumour

See page 4 for more about fair tests and variables.

1) Results from <u>experiments</u> in <u>laboratories</u> are <u>great</u>. A lab is the easiest place to <u>control variables</u> so that they're all kept <u>constant</u> (except for the one you're investigating). This makes it easier to carry out a <u>FAIR TEST</u>.

2) For things that you <u>can't investigate in the lab</u> (e.g. climate) you conduct <u>scientific studies</u>. As many of the variables as possible are controlled, to make it a fair test.

3) Old wives' tales, rumours, hearsay, "what someone said", and so on, should be taken with a pinch of salt. Without any evidence they're <u>NOT scientific</u> — they're just <u>opinions</u>.

The Bigger the Sample Size the Better

1) Data based on <u>small samples</u> isn't as good as data based on large samples. A sample should be <u>representative</u> of the <u>whole population</u> (i.e. it should share as many of the various characteristics in the population as possible) — a small sample can't do that as well.

2) The <u>bigger</u> the sample size the <u>better</u>, but scientists have to be <u>realistic</u> when choosing how big. For example, if you were studying how lifestyle affects people's weight it'd be great to study everyone in the UK (a huge sample), but it'd take ages and cost a bomb. Studying a thousand people is more realistic.

Evidence Needs to be Reliable (Repeatable and Reproducible)

Evidence is only <u>reliable</u> if it can be <u>repeated</u> (during an experiment) AND <u>other scientists can reproduce it too</u> (in other experiments). If it's not reliable, you can't believe it.

> RELIABLE means that the data can be <u>repeated, and reproduced by others</u>.

<u>EXAMPLE:</u> In 1998, a scientist claimed that he'd found a link between the <u>MMR vaccine</u> (for measles, mumps and rubella) and <u>autism</u>. As a result, many parents stopped their children from having the vaccine — which led to a <u>big rise</u> in the number of children catching <u>measles</u>. However, <u>no other scientist</u> has been able to <u>repeat the results</u> since — they just <u>weren't reliable</u>. Health authorities have now concluded that the vaccine is <u>safe</u> to use.

Evidence Also Needs to Be Valid

> VALID means that the data is <u>reliable</u> AND <u>answers the original question</u>.

EXAMPLE: DO MOBILE PHONES CAUSE BRAIN TUMOURS?
Some studies have found that people who use <u>mobile phones regularly</u> are more likely to develop <u>brain tumours</u>. What they'd actually found was a <u>correlation</u> (relationship) between the variables "<u>use of mobile phones</u>" and "<u>development of brain tumours</u>" — they found that as one changed, so did the other. But this evidence is <u>not enough</u> to say that using a mobile phone <u>causes</u> brain tumours, as other explanations might be possible. For example, <u>age</u>, <u>gender</u> and <u>family history</u> can all <u>increase</u> the risk of developing a brain tumour. So these studies don't show a definite link and so don't <u>answer the original question</u>.

RRRR — Remember, Reliable means Repeatable and Reproducible...

By now you should have realised how <u>important</u> trustworthy <u>evidence</u> is (even more important than a good supply of spot cream). Unfortunately, you need to know loads more about fair tests and experiments — see p.4-8.

Bias, Issues and Unanswerable Questions

It isn't all hunky-dory in the world of science — there are some problems...

Scientific Evidence can be Presented in a Biased Way

1) People who want to make a point can sometimes present data in a biased way, e.g. they overemphasise a relationship in the data. (Sometimes without knowing they're doing it.)

2) And there are all sorts of reasons why people might want to do this — for example...

- They want to keep the organisation or company that's funding the research happy. (If the results aren't what they'd like they might not give them any more money to fund further research.)
- Governments might want to persuade voters, other governments, journalists, etc.
- Companies might want to 'big up' their products. Or make impressive safety claims.
- Environmental campaigners might want to persuade people to behave differently.

Scientific Developments are Great, but they can Raise Issues

Scientific knowledge is increased by doing experiments. And this knowledge leads to scientific developments, e.g. new technologies or new advice. These developments can create issues though. For example:

Economic issues: Society can't always afford to do things scientists recommend (e.g. investing heavily in alternative energy sources) without cutting back elsewhere.

Social issues: Decisions based on scientific evidence affect people — e.g. should fossil fuels be taxed more highly (to invest in alternative energy)? Should alcohol be banned (to prevent health problems)? Would the effect on people's lifestyles be acceptable...

Environmental issues: Genetically modified crops may help us produce more food — but some people think they could cause environmental problems.

Ethical issues: There are a lot of things that scientific developments have made possible, but should we do them? E.g. clone humans, develop better nuclear weapons.

Some Questions Are Unanswered by Science, some are Unanswerable

1) At the moment scientists don't all agree on some things (e.g. the likely impacts of global warming, or what the Universe is made of) because there isn't enough reliable and valid evidence.

2) But eventually, we probably will be able to answer these questions once and for all... All we need is more evidence.

3) However, the question of whether something is morally or ethically right or wrong can't be answered by experiments — there is no "right" or "wrong" answer.

4) The best we can do is get a consensus from society — a judgement that most people are more or less happy to live by. Science can provide more information to help people make this judgement, and the judgement might change over time. But in the end it's up to people and their conscience.

Chips or rice? — totally unanswerable by science...

Right — get this straight in your head — science can't tell you whether you should or shouldn't do something. That kind of thing is up to you and society to decide. There are tons of questions that science might be able to answer in the future — like whatever happened to those pink stripy socks with Santa on that I used to have.

How Science Works

Designing Investigations

Dig out your lab coat and dust down your badly-scratched safety goggles... it's investigation time.
You need to know a shed load about <u>investigations</u> for your <u>controlled assessment</u> and <u>all your exams</u>.
Investigations include <u>experiments</u> and <u>studies</u>. The next five pages take you from start to finish. Enjoy.

Investigations <u>Produce Evidence</u> to Support <u>or Disprove a Hypothesis</u>

1) Scientists <u>observe</u> things and come up with <u>hypotheses</u> to explain them (see page 1).

2) To figure out whether a hypothesis might be correct or not you need to do an <u>investigation</u> to <u>gather some evidence</u>.

3) The first step is to use the hypothesis to come up with a <u>prediction</u> — a statement about what you <u>think will happen</u> that you can <u>test</u>.

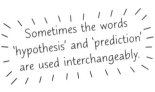
Sometimes the words 'hypothesis' and 'prediction' are used interchangeably.

5) Investigations are used to see if there are <u>patterns</u> or <u>relationships between</u> <u>two variables</u>. For example, to see if there's a pattern or relationship between the variables 'having spots' and 'nose picking'.

6) The investigation has to be a <u>FAIR TEST</u> to make sure the evidence is <u>reliable</u> and <u>valid</u>...

To Make an Investigation a <u>Fair Test</u> You Have to <u>Control the Variables</u>

1) In a lab experiment you usually <u>change one variable</u> and <u>measure</u> how it affects the <u>other variable</u>.

> **EXAMPLE:** you might change only the temperature of a chemical reaction and measure how this affects the rate of reaction.

2) To make it a fair test <u>everything else</u> that could affect the results should <u>stay the same</u> (otherwise you can't tell if the thing you're changing is causing the results or not — the data won't be reliable or valid).

> **EXAMPLE continued:** you need to keep the concentration of the reactants the same, otherwise you won't know if any change in the rate of reaction is caused by the change in temperature, or a difference in reactant concentration.

3) The variable you CHANGE is called the INDEPENDENT variable.

4) The variable you MEASURE is called the DEPENDENT variable.

5) The variables that you KEEP THE SAME are called CONTROL variables.

> **EXAMPLE continued:**
> Independent variable = temperature
> Dependent variable = rate of reaction
> Control variables = concentration of reactants, volume of reactants, etc.

Trial Runs <u>help Figure out the Range and Interval</u> of Variable Values

1) It's a good idea to do a <u>trial run</u> first — a <u>quick version</u> of your experiment.

2) Trial runs are used to figure out the <u>range</u> of variable values used in the proper experiment (the upper and lower limit). If you <u>don't</u> get a <u>change</u> in the dependent variable at the lower values in the trial run, you might <u>narrow the</u> range in the proper experiment. But if you still get a <u>big change</u> at the upper values you might <u>increase</u> the range.

> **EXAMPLE continued:**
> • You might do a trial run with a range of 10-50 °C. If there was no reaction at the lower end (e.g. 10-20 °C), you might narrow the range to 20-50 °C for the proper experiment.
> • If using 1 °C intervals doesn't give you much change in the rate of reaction each time you might decide to use 5 °C intervals, e.g 20, 25, 30, 35, 40, 45, 50 °C...

3) And trial runs can be used to figure out the <u>interval</u> (gaps) between the values too. The intervals can't be too small (otherwise the experiment would take ages), or too big (otherwise you might miss something).

4) Trial runs can also help you figure out <u>how many times</u> the experiment has to be <u>repeated</u> to get reliable results. E.g. if you repeat it three times and the <u>results</u> are all <u>similar</u>, then three repeats is enough.

Designing Investigations

It Can Be Hard to Control the Variables in a Study

It's important that a study is a fair test, just like a lab experiment. It's a lot trickier to control the variables in a study than it is in a lab experiment though (see previous page). Sometimes you can't control them all, but you can use a control group to help. This is a group of whatever you're studying (people, plants, lemmings, etc.) that's kept under the same conditions as the group in the experiment, but doesn't have anything done to it.

EXAMPLE: If you're studying the effect of light on plant growth, one plant will be grown in the dark while another plant will be left to grow in daylight. The plants must be the same species and the other variables (e.g. temperature, water, nutrients) must all be kept the same. The plant grown in the daylight is the control plant — if it grows normally then you know that light is the only variable affecting the other plant.

Investigations Can be Hazardous

1) A hazard is something that can potentially cause harm.
2) Hazards include microorganisms, chemicals, fire and electricity.
3) Scientists need to manage the risk of hazards by doing things to reduce them. For example, if you're working with sulfuric acid, always wear gloves and safety goggles. This will reduce the risk of the acid coming into contact with your skin and eyes.

Hmm... Where did my bacteria sample go?

Your Data Should be as Reliable, Accurate and Precise as Possible

1) To improve reliability you need to repeat the readings and calculate the mean (average). You need to repeat each reading at least three times.
2) To make sure your results are reliable you can cross check them by taking a second set of readings with another instrument (or a different observer).
3) Checking your results match with secondary sources, e.g. other studies, also increases the reliability of your data.
4) Your data also needs to be ACCURATE. Really accurate results are those that are really close to the true answer.
5) Your data also needs to be PRECISE. Precise results are ones where the data is all really close to the mean (i.e. not spread out).

Repeat	Data set 1	Data set 2
1	12	11
2	14	17
3	13	14
Mean	13	14

Data set 1 is more precise than data set 2.

Your Equipment has to be Right for the Job

1) The measuring equipment you use has to be sensitive enough to measure the changes you're looking for. For example, if you need to measure changes of 1 ml you need to use a measuring cylinder that can measure in 1 ml steps — it'd be no good trying with one that only measures 10 ml steps.
2) The smallest change a measuring instrument can detect is called its RESOLUTION. E.g. some mass balances have a resolution of 1 g, some have a resolution of 0.1 g, and some are even more sensitive.
3) Also, equipment needs to be calibrated so that your data is more accurate. E.g. mass balances need to be set to zero before you start weighing things.

You won't get a trial run at the exam, so get learnin'...

All this info needs to be firmly lodged in your memory. Learn the names of the different variables — if you remember that the variable you chaNge is called the iNdependent variable, you can figure out the other ones.

Errors and Presenting Data

After designing an investigation that's so beautiful people will marvel at it for years to come, you'll need to <u>present</u> that glorious data. But not checking your data for <u>errors</u> first would be a bit of an, err, error.

You Need to Look out for Errors and Anomalous Results

1) The results of your experiment will always <u>vary a bit</u> because of <u>random errors</u> — tiny differences caused by things like <u>human errors</u> in <u>measuring</u>.

2) You can <u>reduce</u> their effect by taking many readings and calculating the <u>mean</u>.

3) If the <u>same error</u> is made every time, it's called a SYSTEMATIC ERROR. For example, if you measured from the very end of your ruler instead of from the 0 cm mark every time, all your measurements would be a bit small.

Repeating the experiment in the exact same way and calculating an average won't correct a systematic error.

4) Just to make things more complicated, if a systematic error is caused by using <u>equipment</u> that <u>isn't zeroed properly</u> it's called a ZERO ERROR. For example, if a mass balance always reads 1 gram before you put anything on it, all your measurements will be 1 gram too heavy.

5) You can <u>compensate</u> for some systematic errors if you know about them though, e.g. if your mass balance always reads 1 gram before you put anything on it you can subtract 1 gram from all your results.

6) Sometimes you get a result that <u>doesn't seem to fit in</u> with the rest at all.

7) These results are called ANOMALOUS RESULTS.

8) You should investigate them and try to <u>work out what happened</u>. If you can work out what happened (e.g. you measured something totally wrong) you can <u>ignore</u> them when processing your results.

Park	Number of pigeons	Number of crazy tramps
A	28	1
B	42	2
C	1127	0

Data Needs to be Organised

1) Tables are dead useful for <u>organising data</u>.

2) When you draw a table <u>use a ruler</u>, make sure <u>each column</u> has a <u>heading</u> (including the <u>units</u>) and keep it neat and tidy.

3) Annoyingly, tables are about as useful as a chocolate teapot for showing <u>patterns</u> or <u>relationships</u> in data. You need to use some kind of graph for that.

If Your Data Comes in Categories, Present It in a Bar Chart

1) If the independent variable is <u>categoric</u> (comes in distinct categories, e.g. blood types, metals) you should use a <u>bar chart</u> to display the data.

2) There are some <u>golden rules</u> you need to follow for <u>drawing</u> bar charts:

Remember to include the <u>units</u>.

If you've got more than one set of data <u>include a key</u>.

Ice Cream Sales in Froggartland and Broccoliland

□ Froggartland
▨ Broccoliland

Number sold (thousands)

Chocolate   Mint   Strawberry   Broccoli
Ice cream flavour

<u>Label both axes</u>.

Draw it nice and <u>big</u> (covering at least half of the graph paper).

Leave a <u>gap between</u> different categories.

Zero error — sounds like a Bruce Willis film...

Make sure you know your <u>systematic</u> errors from your <u>zero</u> errors. Also, you might think, 'Yer, yer, I know how to <u>draw tables</u> and <u>bar charts</u>', but to make the examiners happy you've got to draw them just right — learn the rules.

Presenting Data

Scientists just <u>love</u> presenting data as <u>line graphs</u> (weirdos)...

If Your Data is Continuous, Plot a Line Graph

1) If the independent variable is <u>continuous</u> (numerical data that can have any value within a range, e.g. length, volume, temperature) you should use a <u>line graph</u> to display the data.

2) Here are the <u>rules</u> for <u>drawing</u> line graphs:

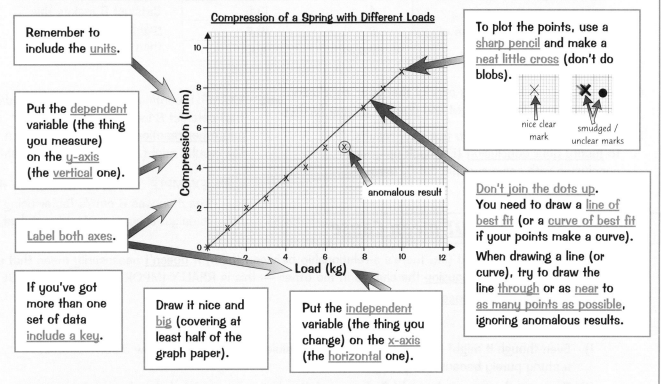

Remember to include the <u>units</u>.

Put the <u>dependent</u> variable (the thing you measure) on the <u>y-axis</u> (the <u>vertical</u> one).

<u>Label both axes</u>.

If you've got more than one set of data <u>include a key</u>.

Draw it nice and <u>big</u> (covering at least half of the graph paper).

Put the <u>independent</u> variable (the thing you change) on the <u>x-axis</u> (the <u>horizontal</u> one).

To plot the points, use a <u>sharp pencil</u> and make a <u>neat little cross</u> (don't do blobs).

nice clear mark — smudged / unclear marks

anomalous result

<u>Don't join the dots up</u>. You need to draw a <u>line of best fit</u> (or a <u>curve of best fit</u> if your points make a curve). When drawing a line (or curve), try to draw the line <u>through</u> or as <u>near</u> to as many points as possible, ignoring anomalous results.

3) Line graphs are used to <u>show the relationship</u> between two variables (just like other graphs).

4) Data can show <u>three</u> different types of correlation (relationship):

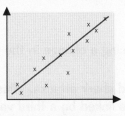 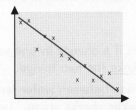 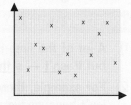

<u>POSITIVE</u> correlation — as one variable <u>increases</u> the other <u>increases</u>.

<u>NEGATIVE</u> correlation — as one variable <u>increases</u> the other <u>decreases</u>.

<u>NO</u> correlation — there's <u>no relationship</u> between the two variables.

5) You need to be able to describe the following relationships on line graphs too:

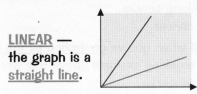 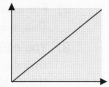

<u>LINEAR</u> — the graph is a <u>straight line</u>.

<u>DIRECTLY PROPORTIONAL</u> — the graph is a <u>straight line</u> where both variables increase (or decrease) in the <u>same ratio</u>.

There's a positive correlation between revision and boredom...

...but there's also a positive correlation between <u>revision</u> and getting a <u>better mark in the exam</u>. Cover the page and write down the <u>eight things</u> you need to remember when <u>drawing graphs</u>. No sneaky peeking either — I saw you.

Drawing Conclusions

Congratulations — you've made it to the <u>final step</u> of a gruelling investigation — <u>drawing conclusions</u>.

You Can Only Conclude What the Data Shows and NO MORE

1) Drawing conclusions might seem pretty straightforward — you just <u>look at your data</u> and <u>say what pattern or relationship you see</u> between the dependent and independent variables.

EXAMPLE: The table on the right shows the rate of a reaction in the presence of two different catalysts.

Catalyst	Rate of reaction (cm³/s)
A	13.5
B	19.5
No catalyst	5.5

CONCLUSION:
Catalyst <u>B</u> makes <u>this reaction</u> go faster than catalyst A.

2) But you've got to be really careful that your conclusion <u>matches the data</u> you've got and <u>doesn't go any further</u>.

3) You also need to be able to <u>use your results</u> to <u>justify your conclusion</u> (i.e. back up your conclusion with some specific data).

EXAMPLE continued: You <u>can't</u> conclude that catalyst B increases the rate of <u>any other reaction</u> more than catalyst A — the results might be completely different.

EXAMPLE continued: The rate of this reaction was 6 cm³/s faster using catalyst B compared with catalyst A.

Correlation DOES NOT mean Cause

1) If two things are correlated (i.e. there's a relationship between them) it <u>doesn't</u> necessarily mean that a change in one variable is <u>causing</u> the change in the other — this is REALLY IMPORTANT, DON'T FORGET IT.

2) There are <u>three possible reasons</u> for a correlation:

① CHANCE

1) Even though it might seem a bit weird, it's possible that two things show a correlation in a study purely because of <u>chance</u>.

2) For example, one study might find a correlation between people's hair colour and how good they are at frisbee. But other scientists don't get a correlation when they investigate it — the results of the first study are just a fluke.

② LINKED BY A 3rd VARIABLE

1) A lot of the time it may <u>look</u> as if a change in one variable is causing a change in the other, but it <u>isn't</u> — a <u>third variable links</u> the two things.

2) For example, there's a correlation between water temperature and shark attacks. This obviously isn't because warmer water makes sharks crazy. Instead, they're linked by a third variable — the number of people swimming (more people swim when the water's hotter, and with more people in the water you get more shark attacks).

③ CAUSE

1) Sometimes a change in one variable does <u>cause</u> a change in the other.

2) For example, there's a correlation between smoking and lung cancer. This is because chemicals in tobacco smoke cause lung cancer.

3) You can only conclude that a correlation is due to cause when you've <u>controlled all the variables</u> that could, just could, be affecting the result. (For the smoking example above this would include things like age and exposure to other things that cause cancer).

I conclude that this page is a bit dull...

...although, just because I find it dull doesn't mean that I can conclude it's dull (you might think it's the most interesting thing since that kid got his head stuck in the railings near school). In the exams you could be given a <u>conclusion</u> and asked <u>whether some data supports it</u> — so make sure you understand <u>how far conclusions can go</u>.

Controlled Assessment (ISA)

Controlled Assessment involves <u>doing an experiment</u> and <u>answering two question papers on it</u> under exam conditions. Sounds thrilling.

There are Two Sections in the Controlled Assessment

① Planning

Before you do the Section 1 question paper you'll be given time to do some <u>research</u> into the topic that's been set — you'll need to develop a <u>hypothesis/prediction</u> and come up with <u>two</u> different methods to test it. In your research, you should use a variety of <u>different sources</u> (e.g. the internet, textbooks etc.). You'll need to be able to <u>outline both methods</u> and say which one is <u>best</u> (and why it's the best one) and describe your preferred method in <u>detail</u>. You're allowed to write <u>notes</u> about your two methods on <u>one side of A4</u> and have them with you for both question papers. In Section 1, you could be asked things like:

1) What your <u>hypothesis/prediction</u> is.
2) What variables you're going to <u>control</u> (and <u>how</u> you're going to control them).
3) What <u>measurements</u> you're going to take.
4) What <u>range</u> and <u>interval</u> of values you will use for the <u>independent variable</u>.
5) How you'd figure out the range and interval using a <u>trial run</u> (sometimes called a 'preliminary investigation' in the question papers). See page 4 for more.
6) How many times you're going to <u>repeat</u> the experiment — a minimum of <u>three</u> is a good idea.
7) What <u>equipment</u> you're going to use (and <u>why</u> that equipment is <u>right for the job</u>).
8) <u>How to carry out</u> the experiment, i.e. what you do first, what you do second...
9) What <u>hazards</u> are involved in doing the experiment, and <u>how to reduce them</u>.
10) What <u>table</u> you'll draw to put your results in. See page 6 for how to draw one that examiners will love.

There's lots of help on all of these things on pages 4-7.

When you've done the planning and completed the first question paper you'll actually <u>do the experiment</u>. Then you'll have to <u>present your data</u>. Make sure you use the <u>right type of graph</u>, and you <u>draw it properly</u> — see pages 6-7 for help. After that it's onto the Section 2 question paper...

② Drawing Conclusions and Evaluating

For the Section 2 question paper you have to do these things for <u>your experiment</u>:

1) <u>Analyse</u> and <u>draw conclusions</u> from your results. For this you need to <u>describe the relationship</u> between the variables in <u>detail</u> — see the previous page for how to do this. E.g. 'I found that there is a relationship between picking your nose and having spots. The more often you pick your nose the more spots you'll have. For example, my results showed...'.
2) Say whether your results <u>back up the hypothesis/prediction</u>, and give reasons <u>why</u> or <u>why not</u>. E.g. 'My results did not back up the prediction. The prediction was that picking your nose more has no effect on the number of spots you have. But I found the opposite to be true in my investigation'.
3) <u>Evaluate</u> your experiment. For this you need to <u>suggest ways you could improve your experiment</u>.
   - Comment on your <u>equipment</u> and <u>method</u>, e.g. could you have used more <u>accurate</u> equipment?
   - Make sure you <u>explain how</u> the improvements would give you <u>better data</u> next time.
   - <u>Refer to your results</u>. E.g. 'My data wasn't accurate enough because the mass balance I used only measured in 1 g steps. I could use a more sensitive one next time (e.g. a mass balance that measures in 0.5 g steps) to get more accurate data'.

You'll also be <u>given some secondary data</u> (data collected by someone else) from an experiment on the same topic and asked to <u>analyse it</u>. This just involves doing what you did for your data with the secondary data, e.g. draw conclusions from it.

If that's controlled assessment, I'd hate to see uncontrolled assessment...

That might be an Everest-sized list of stuff, but it's <u>all important</u>. No need to panic at the sight of it though — as long as you've <u>learnt everything</u> on the previous few pages, you should be fine.

Cells

All living things are made of cells. When someone first peered down a microscope at a slice of cork and drew the boxes they saw, little did they know that they'd seen the building blocks of every organism on the planet.

Plant and Animal Cells have Similarities and Differences

Most human cells, like most animal cells, have the following parts — make sure you know them all:

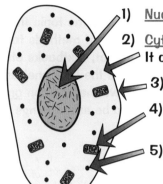

1) Nucleus — contains genetic material that controls the activities of the cell.

2) Cytoplasm — gel-like substance where most of the chemical reactions happen. It contains enzymes (see page 21) that control these chemical reactions.

3) Cell membrane — holds the cell together and controls what goes in and out.

4) Mitochondria — these are where most of the reactions for respiration take place (see page 24). Respiration releases energy that the cell needs to work.

5) Ribosomes — these are where proteins are made in the cell.

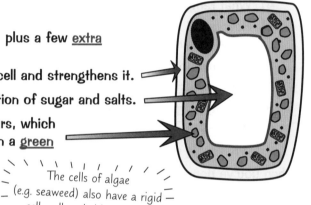

Plant cells usually have all the bits that animal cells have, plus a few extra things that animal cells don't have:

1) Rigid cell wall — made of cellulose. It supports the cell and strengthens it.

2) Permanent vacuole — contains cell sap, a weak solution of sugar and salts.

3) Chloroplasts — these are where photosynthesis occurs, which makes food for the plant (see page 14). They contain a green substance called chlorophyll.

The cells of algae (e.g. seaweed) also have a rigid cell wall and chloroplasts.

Yeast is a Single-Celled Organism

Yeast is a microorganism. A yeast cell has a nucleus, cytoplasm, and a cell membrane surrounded by a cell wall.

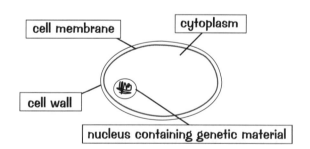

cell membrane | cytoplasm
cell wall
nucleus containing genetic material

Bacterial Cells Have No Nucleus

Bacteria are also single-celled microorganisms.

1) A bacterial cell has cytoplasm and a cell membrane surrounded by a cell wall.

2) The genetic material floats in the cytoplasm because bacterial cells don't have a nucleus.

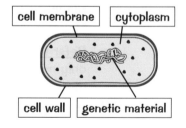

cell membrane | cytoplasm
cell wall | genetic material

There's quite a bit to learn in biology — but that's life, I guess...

On this page are typical cells with all the typical bits you need to know. But cells aren't all the same — they have different structures and produce different substances depending on the job they do.

Diffusion

Particles <u>move about randomly</u>, and after a bit they end up <u>evenly spaced</u>. It's not rocket science, is it...

Don't Be Put Off by the Fancy Word

1) "<u>Diffusion</u>" is simple. It's just the <u>gradual movement</u> of particles from places where there are <u>lots</u> of them to places where there are <u>fewer</u> of them.

2) That's all it is — just the <u>natural tendency</u> for stuff to <u>spread out</u>.

3) Unfortunately you also have to learn the fancy way of saying the same thing, which is this:

> ***DIFFUSION** is the <u>spreading out</u> of <u>particles</u> from an area of <u>HIGH CONCENTRATION</u> to an area of <u>LOW CONCENTRATION</u>*

4) Diffusion happens in both <u>solutions</u> and <u>gases</u> — that's because the particles in these substances are free to <u>move about</u> randomly.

5) The <u>simplest type</u> is when different <u>gases</u> diffuse through each other. This is what's happening when the smell of perfume diffuses through the air in a room:

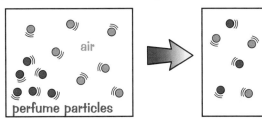

perfume particles diffused in the air

6) The <u>bigger</u> the <u>difference</u> in concentration, the <u>faster</u> the diffusion rate.

Cell Membranes Are Kind of Clever...

1) They're clever because they <u>hold</u> the cell together **BUT** they let stuff <u>in and out</u> as well.

2) Dissolved substances can move in and out of cells by <u>diffusion</u>.

3) Only very <u>small</u> molecules can <u>diffuse</u> through cell membranes though — things like <u>oxygen</u> (needed for respiration — see page 24), <u>glucose</u>, <u>amino acids</u> and <u>water</u>.

4) <u>Big</u> molecules like <u>starch</u> and <u>proteins</u> can't fit through the membrane:

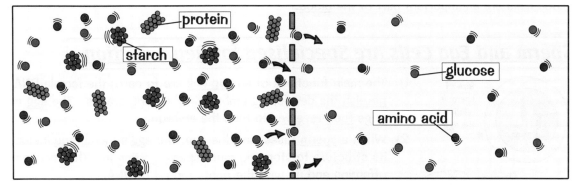

5) Just like with diffusion in air, particles flow through the cell membrane from where there's a <u>high concentration</u> (a lot of them) to where there's a <u>low concentration</u> (not such a lot of them).

6) They're only moving about <u>randomly</u> of course, so they go <u>both</u> ways — but if there are a lot <u>more</u> particles on one side of the membrane, there's a <u>net</u> (overall) movement <u>from</u> that side.

Revision by diffusion — you wish...

Wouldn't that be great — if all the ideas in this book would just gradually drift across into your mind, from an area of <u>high concentration</u> (in the book) to an area of <u>low concentration</u> (in your mind — no offence). Actually, that probably will happen if you read it again. Why don't you give it a go...

Specialised Cells

Page 10 shows the structure of some typical cells. However, most cells are <u>specialised</u> for their specific function, so their structure can vary...

1) <u>Palisade Leaf Cells</u> Are Adapted for <u>Photosynthesis</u>

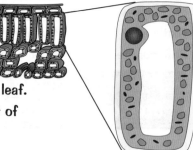

1) Packed with <u>chloroplasts</u> for <u>photosynthesis</u>. More of them are crammed at the <u>top</u> of the cell — so they're nearer the <u>light</u>.
2) <u>Tall</u> shape means a lot of <u>surface area</u> exposed down the side for <u>absorbing CO$_2$</u> from the air in the leaf.
3) <u>Thin</u> shape means that you can pack loads of them in at the top of a leaf.

Palisade leaf cells are grouped together at the top of the leaf where most of the <u>photosynthesis</u> happens.

2) <u>Guard Cells</u> Are Adapted to <u>Open and Close Pores</u>

1) Special kidney shape which <u>opens</u> and <u>closes</u> the <u>stomata</u> (pores) in a leaf.
2) When the plant has <u>lots</u> of water the guard cells fill with it and go plump and <u>turgid</u>. This makes the stomata <u>open</u> so <u>gases</u> can be exchanged for <u>photosynthesis</u>.
3) When the plant is <u>short</u> of water, the guard cells lose water and become <u>flaccid</u>, making the stomata <u>close</u>. This helps stop too much water vapour <u>escaping</u>.
4) <u>Thin</u> outer walls and <u>thickened</u> inner walls make the opening and closing work.
5) They're also <u>sensitive to light</u> and <u>close at night</u> to save water without losing out on photosynthesis.

Guard cells are therefore adapted to their function of allowing <u>gas exchange</u> and <u>controlling water loss</u> within a <u>leaf</u>.

3) <u>Red Blood Cells</u> Are Adapted to <u>Carry Oxygen</u>

1) <u>Concave</u> shape gives a big <u>surface area</u> for absorbing <u>oxygen</u>. It also helps them pass <u>smoothly</u> through <u>capillaries</u> to reach body cells.
2) They're packed with <u>haemoglobin</u> — the pigment that absorbs the oxygen.
3) They have <u>no nucleus</u>, to leave even more room for haemoglobin.

Red blood cells are an important part of the <u>blood</u>.

4) <u>Sperm</u> and <u>Egg Cells</u> Are Specialised for <u>Reproduction</u>

Size of sperm in relation to the egg

Egg

Sperm

1) The main functions of an <u>egg cell</u> are to carry the female DNA and to <u>nourish</u> the developing embryo in the early stages. The egg cell contains huge <u>food reserves</u> to feed the embryo.
2) When a <u>sperm</u> fuses with the egg, the egg's <u>membrane</u> instantly <u>changes</u> its structure to stop any more sperm getting in. This makes sure the offspring end up with the <u>right amount</u> of DNA.
3) The function of a <u>sperm</u> is basically to get the <u>male DNA</u> to the <u>female DNA</u>. It has a <u>long tail</u> and a <u>streamlined head</u> to help it <u>swim</u> to the egg. There are a lot of <u>mitochondria</u> in the cell to provide the <u>energy</u> needed.
4) Sperm also carry <u>enzymes</u> in their heads to digest through the egg cell membrane.

Sperm and eggs are very important cells in <u>reproduction</u>.

Beans, flying saucers, tadpoles — cells are masters of disguise...

These cells all have all the bits shown on page 10, even though they look completely different and do <u>totally different jobs</u>. Apart from red blood cells that is, which are a bit special, e.g. they don't have a nucleus.

<u>*Cell Organisation*</u>

How, you might wonder, does having all these <u>specialised cells</u> mean you end up with a working <u>human</u> or <u>squirrel</u>... the answer's <u>organisation</u>. Otherwise you'd just have a meaty splodge.

<u>Large Multicellular Organisms</u> *are Made Up of* Organ Systems

1) As you know from the previous page, <u>specialised cells</u> carry out a <u>particular function</u>.
2) The <u>process</u> by which cells become specialised for a particular job is called <u>differentiation</u>.
3) Differentiation occurs during the <u>development</u> of a multicellular organism.
4) These <u>specialised cells</u> form <u>tissues</u>, which form <u>organs</u>, which form <u>organ systems</u> (see below).
5) <u>Large multicellular organisms</u> (e.g. squirrels) have different <u>systems</u> inside them for <u>exchanging</u> and <u>transporting</u> materials.

<u>Epithelial cell</u>

less than 0.1 mm

<u>Similar Cells</u> *are Organised into* Tissues

A <u>tissue</u> is a <u>group</u> of <u>similar cells</u> that work together to carry out a particular <u>function</u>. It can include <u>more than one type</u> of cell. In <u>mammals</u> (like humans), examples of tissues include:

1) <u>Muscular tissue</u>, which <u>contracts</u> (shortens) to <u>move</u> whatever it's attached to.
2) <u>Glandular tissue</u>, which <u>makes</u> and <u>secretes</u> chemicals like <u>enzymes</u> and <u>hormones</u>.
3) <u>Epithelial tissue</u>, which <u>covers</u> some parts of the body, e.g. the <u>inside</u> of the <u>gut</u>.

<u>Epithelial tissue</u>

<u>Tissues</u> *are Organised into* Organs

An <u>organ</u> is a group of <u>different tissues</u> that work together to perform a certain <u>function</u>. For example, the <u>stomach</u> is an organ made of these tissues:

1) <u>Muscular tissue</u>, which moves the stomach wall to <u>churn up the food</u>.
2) <u>Glandular tissue</u>, which makes <u>digestive juices</u> to digest food.
3) <u>Epithelial tissue</u>, which covers the <u>outside</u> and <u>inside</u> of the stomach.

<u>Stomach</u>

about 10 cm (over 1000 times longer than an epithelial cell)

<u>Organs</u> *are Organised into* Organ Systems

An <u>organ system</u> is a <u>group of organs</u> working together to perform a particular <u>function</u>. For example, the <u>digestive system</u> (found in humans and mammals) <u>breaks down food</u> and is made up of these organs:

1) <u>Glands</u> (e.g. the <u>pancreas</u> and <u>salivary glands</u>), which produce <u>digestive juices</u>.
2) The <u>stomach</u> and <u>small intestine</u>, which <u>digest</u> food.
3) The <u>liver</u>, which produces <u>bile</u>.
4) The <u>small intestine</u>, which <u>absorbs</u> soluble <u>food</u> molecules.
5) The <u>large intestine</u>, which <u>absorbs water</u> from undigested food, leaving <u>faeces</u>.

The digestive system <u>exchanges materials</u> with the <u>environment</u> by <u>taking in nutrients</u> and <u>releasing substances</u> such as bile. There's more on the digestive system on pages 22-23.

Salivary glands

Liver

<u>Digestive system</u>
Stomach
Pancreas
Small intestine
Large intestine

You need to know where these organs are on a diagram — see page 23 too.

<u>Soft and quilted — the best kind of tissues...</u>

OK, <u>cells</u> are organised into <u>tissues</u>, the tissues into <u>organs</u>, and the organs into a whole <u>organism</u>. Or, to put it another way, an <u>organism</u> consists of <u>organs</u> which are made of <u>tissues</u> which are groups of <u>cells</u> working together.

Plant Structure and Photosynthesis

First, a photosynthesis equation. You must learn the photosynthesis equation. Learn it so well that you'll still remember it when you're 109. Then, at the bottom of this page is a lovely leaf pic. Aaaah.

Plant Cells Are Organised Into Tissues And Organs Too

Plants are made of organs like stems, roots and leaves. These organs are made of tissues.
For example, leaves are made of:

1) Mesophyll tissue — this is where most of the photosynthesis in a plant occurs.
2) Xylem and phloem — they transport things like water, mineral ions and sucrose around the plant.
3) Epidermal tissue — this covers the whole plant.

If you're wondering where these tissues are in a plant, check out the leaf diagram at the bottom of the page.

Learn the Equation for Photosynthesis:

$$\text{Carbon dioxide} + \text{water} \xrightarrow[\text{chlorophyll}]{\text{SUNLIGHT}} \text{glucose} + \text{oxygen}$$

Photosynthesis Produces Glucose Using Sunlight

1) Photosynthesis is the process that produces 'food' in plants and algae. The 'food' it produces is glucose.
2) Photosynthesis happens inside the chloroplasts.
3) Chloroplasts contain a green substance called chlorophyll, which absorbs sunlight and uses its energy to convert carbon dioxide (from the air) and water (from the soil) into glucose. Oxygen is also produced as a by-product.
4) Photosynthesis happens in the leaves of all green plants — this is largely what the leaves are for. Below is a cross-section of a leaf showing the four raw materials needed for photosynthesis.

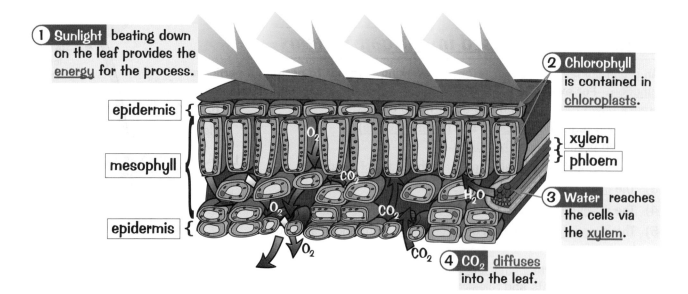

① Sunlight beating down on the leaf provides the energy for the process.
② Chlorophyll is contained in chloroplasts.
epidermis
mesophyll
epidermis
xylem
phloem
③ Water reaches the cells via the xylem.
④ CO_2 diffuses into the leaf.

Now you'll have something to bore the great-grandkids with...

You'll be able to tell them how in your day, all you needed was a bit of carbon dioxide and some water and you could make your own entertainment. See, when you're 109 you're allowed to get a bit confused, but in the middle of an exam you most certainly are not. So if you don't know it, learn it. (And if you do, learn it again anyway.)

The Rate of Photosynthesis

The rate of photosynthesis is affected by the intensity of <u>light</u>, the volume of <u>CO_2</u>, and the <u>temperature</u>. Plants also need <u>water</u> for photosynthesis, but when a plant is so short of water that it becomes the <u>limiting factor</u> in photosynthesis, it's already in such <u>trouble</u> that this is the least of its worries.

The Limiting Factor Depends on the Conditions

1) Any of these three factors can become the <u>limiting factor</u>. This just means that it's stopping photosynthesis from happening any <u>faster</u>.

2) Which factor is limiting at a particular time depends on the <u>environmental conditions</u>:
   - at <u>night</u> it's pretty obvious that <u>light</u> is the limiting factor,
   - in <u>winter</u> it's often the <u>temperature</u>,
   - if it's warm enough and bright enough, the amount of <u>CO_2</u> is usually limiting.

You can do <u>experiments</u> to work out the <u>ideal conditions</u> for photosynthesis in a particular plant. The easiest type to use is a water plant like <u>Canadian pondweed</u> — you can easily measure the amount of <u>oxygen produced</u> in a given time to show how <u>fast</u> photosynthesis is happening (remember, oxygen is made during photosynthesis).

You could either count the <u>bubbles</u> given off, or if you want to be a bit more <u>accurate</u> you could <u>collect</u> the oxygen in a <u>gas syringe</u>.

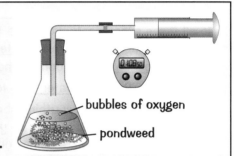
bubbles of oxygen
pondweed

Three Important Graphs for Rate of Photosynthesis

1) Not Enough Light Slows Down the Rate of Photosynthesis

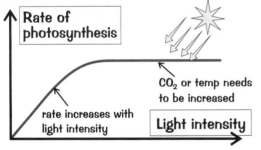

Rate of photosynthesis
CO_2 or temp needs to be increased
rate increases with light intensity
Light intensity

1) Light provides the <u>energy</u> needed for photosynthesis.
2) As the <u>light level</u> is raised, the rate of photosynthesis <u>increases steadily</u> — but only up to a <u>certain point</u>.
3) Beyond that, it <u>won't</u> make any difference because then it'll be either the <u>temperature</u> or the <u>CO_2 level</u> which is the limiting factor.
4) In the lab you can change the light intensity by <u>moving a lamp</u> closer to or further away from your plant.

5) But if you just plot the rate of photosynthesis against "distance of lamp from the beaker", you get a <u>weird-shaped graph</u>. To get a graph like the one above you either need to <u>measure</u> the light intensity at the beaker using a <u>light meter</u> or do a bit of nifty maths with your results.

2) Too Little Carbon Dioxide Also Slows it Down

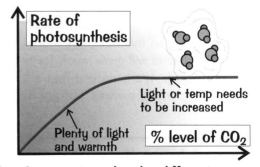

Rate of photosynthesis
Light or temp needs to be increased
Plenty of light and warmth
% level of CO_2

1) CO_2 is one of the <u>raw materials</u> needed for photosynthesis.
2) As with light intensity the amount of <u>CO_2</u> will only increase the rate of photosynthesis up to a point. After this the graph <u>flattens out</u> showing that CO_2 is no longer the <u>limiting factor</u>.
3) As long as <u>light</u> and <u>CO_2</u> are in plentiful supply then the factor limiting photosynthesis must be <u>temperature</u>.
4) There are loads of different ways to control the amount of CO_2. One way is to dissolve different amounts of <u>sodium hydrogencarbonate</u> in the water, which <u>gives off</u> CO_2.

The Rate of Photosynthesis

3) The Temperature has to be Just Right

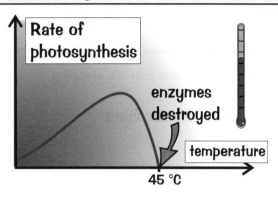

Rate of photosynthesis

enzymes destroyed

temperature

45 °C

1) Usually, if the temperature is the limiting factor it's because it's too low — the enzymes needed for photosynthesis work more slowly at low temperatures.

2) But if the plant gets too hot, the enzymes it needs for photosynthesis and its other reactions will be damaged.

3) This happens at about 45 °C (which is pretty hot for outdoors, although greenhouses can get that hot if you're not careful).

4) Experimentally, the best way to control the temperature of the flask is to put it in a water bath.

In all these experiments, you have to try and keep all the variables constant apart from the one you're investigating, so it's a fair test:

- use a bench lamp to control the intensity of the light (careful not to block the light with anything)
- keep the flask in a water bath to help keep the temperature constant
- you can't really do anything about the CO_2 levels — you just have to use a large flask, and do the experiments as quickly as you can, so that the plant doesn't use up too much of the CO_2 in the flask. If you're using sodium hydrogencarbonate make sure it's changed each time.

You can Artificially Create the Ideal Conditions for Farming

1) The most common way to artificially create the ideal environment for plants is to grow them in a greenhouse.

2) Greenhouses help to trap the sun's heat, and make sure that the temperature doesn't become limiting. In winter a farmer or gardener might use a heater as well to keep the temperature at the ideal level. In summer it could get too hot, so they might use shades and ventilation to cool things down.

3) Light is always needed for photosynthesis, so commercial farmers often supply artificial light after the Sun goes down to give their plants more quality photosynthesis time.

4) Farmers and gardeners can also increase the level of carbon dioxide in the greenhouse. A fairly common way is to use a paraffin heater to heat the greenhouse. As the paraffin burns, it makes carbon dioxide as a by-product.

5) Keeping plants enclosed in a greenhouse also makes it easier to keep them free from pests and diseases. The farmer can add fertilisers to the soil as well, to provide all the minerals needed for healthy growth.

6) Sorting all this out costs money — but if the farmer can keep the conditions just right for photosynthesis, the plants will grow much faster and a decent crop can be harvested much more often, which can then be sold. It's important that a farmer supplies just the right amount of heat, light, etc. — enough to make the plants grow well, but not more than the plants need, as this would just be wasting money.

Don't blame it on the sunshine, don't blame it on the CO_2...

...don't blame it on the temperature, blame it on the plant. Right, and now you'll never forget the three limiting factors in photosynthesis. No... well, make sure you read these pages over and over again till you do. With your newly found knowledge of photosynthesis you could take over the world...

How Plants Use Glucose

Once plants have made glucose by photosynthesis (see p.14), there are a few ways they can use it.

① For Respiration

1) Plants manufacture glucose in their leaves.
2) They then use some of the glucose for respiration (see page 24).
3) This releases energy which enables them to convert the rest of the glucose into various other useful substances, which they can use to build new cells and grow.
4) To produce some of these substances they also need to gather a few minerals from the soil.

② Making Cell Walls

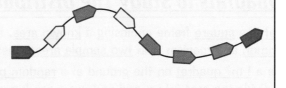

Glucose is converted into cellulose for making strong cell walls (see page 10), especially in a rapidly growing plant.

③ Making Proteins

Glucose is combined with nitrate ions (absorbed from the soil) to make amino acids, which are then made into proteins.

④ Stored in Seeds

Glucose is turned into lipids (fats and oils) for storing in seeds. Sunflower seeds, for example, contain a lot of oil — we get cooking oil and margarine from them. Seeds also store starch (see below).

Algae also use glucose to make cellulose for cell walls, fats and oils for storage, and amino acids for proteins.

⑤ Stored as Starch

Glucose is turned into starch and stored in roots, stems and leaves, ready for use when photosynthesis isn't happening, like in the winter.
Starch is insoluble which makes it much better for storing than glucose — a cell with lots of glucose in would draw in loads of water and swell up.
Potato and parsnip plants store a lot of starch underground over the winter so a new plant can grow from it the following spring. We eat the swollen storage organs.

For making small ornamental birdcages...

Actually, I made that last one up. I was bored. So there are actually only five things to learn that plants do with glucose. Right, shut the book right now. Or actually, finish reading this and then shut the book. Then write down all five uses of glucose from memory. Bet you forget one. Repeat until you don't.

Distribution of Organisms

This is where the <u>fun</u> starts. Studying <u>ecology</u> gives you the chance to <u>rummage around</u> in bushes, get your hands <u>dirty</u> and look at some <u>real organisms</u>, living in the <u>wild</u>. Hold on to your hats folks...

Organisms Live in Different Places Because The Environment Varies

1) A habitat is the place where an organism <u>lives</u>, e.g. a playing field.

2) The <u>distribution</u> of an organism is <u>where</u> an organism is <u>found</u>, e.g. in a part of the playing field.

3) Where an organism is found is affected by <u>environmental factors</u> such as:

- <u>Temperature</u>.
- Availability of <u>water</u>.
- Availability of <u>oxygen</u> and <u>carbon dioxide</u>.
- Availability of <u>nutrients</u>.
- Amount of <u>light</u>.

4) An organism might be <u>more common</u> in <u>one area</u> than another due to <u>differences</u> in <u>environmental factors</u> between the two areas. For example, in a field, you might find that daisies are <u>more common</u> in the open, than under trees, because there's <u>more light</u> available in the open.

5) There are a couple of ways to <u>study</u> the distribution of an organism. You can:

- <u>measure</u> how common an organism is in <u>two sample areas</u> (e.g. using <u>quadrats</u>) and compare them.
- study how the distribution <u>changes</u> across an area e.g. by placing quadrats along a <u>transect</u> (p.19).

Use Quadrats to Study The Distribution of Small Organisms

A <u>quadrat</u> is a <u>square</u> frame enclosing a <u>known area</u>, e.g. 1 m^2. To compare how common an organism is in <u>two sample areas</u>, just follow these simple steps:

A quadrat

1 m

1 m

1) Place a <u>1 m^2 quadrat</u> on the ground at a <u>random point</u> within the <u>first</u> sample area. E.g. divide the area into a grid and use a random number generator to pick coordinates.

2) <u>Count</u> all the organisms <u>within</u> the quadrat.

3) <u>Repeat</u> steps 1 and 2 as many times as you can.

4) <u>Work out</u> the <u>mean</u> number of organisms per quadrat within the first sample area.

- For example, Anna counted the number of daisies in 7 quadrats within her first sample area and recorded the following results: 18, 20, 22, 23, 23, 23, 25

- Here the MEAN is: $\dfrac{\text{TOTAL number of organisms}}{\text{NUMBER of quadrats}} = \dfrac{154}{7} = \underline{22}$ daisies per quadrat.

- You also need to know about the MODE, which is the MOST COMMON value. In this example it's <u>23</u>.

- And the MEDIAN is the MIDDLE value, when they're in order of size. In this example it's <u>23</u> also.

5) <u>Repeat</u> steps 1 to 4 in the <u>second</u> sample area.

6) Finally <u>compare</u> the two means. E.g. you might find 2 daisies per m^2 in the shade, and 22 daisies per m^2 (lots more) in the open field.

In the Exam You Might Have to Work Out Population Size

To work out the <u>population size</u> of an organism in one sample area:

1) Work out the <u>mean number of organisms per m^2</u>. (If your quadrat has an area of 1 m^2, this is the <u>same</u> as the mean number of organisms per quadrat, worked out above.)

2) Then multiply the <u>mean</u> by the <u>total area</u> (in m^2) of the habitat.

3) E.g. if the area of an open field is 800 m^2, and there are 22 daisies per m^2, then the size of the daisy population is $22 \times 800 = 17\ 600$.

Ben liked looking after his quad-rats.

Drat, drat, and double drat — my favourite use of quadrats...

You must put your quadrat down in a <u>random place</u> before you start counting. Anything, even chucking the quadrat over your shoulder*, is better than plonking it down right on the <u>first big patch</u> of organisms that you see.

*not an invitation to break equipment or maim fellow students etc.

More on The Distribution of Organisms

So, now you think you've learnt all about distribution. Well hold on — there's more ecology fun to be had.

Use Transects to Study The Distribution of Organisms Along a Line

You can use lines called transects to help find out how organisms (like plants) are distributed across an area — e.g. if an organism becomes more or less common as you move from a hedge towards the middle of a field. Here's what to do:

1) Mark out a line in the area you want to study using a tape measure.

2) Then collect data along the line.

3) You can do this by just counting all the organisms you're interested in that touch the line.

4) Or, you can collect data by using quadrats. These can be placed next to each other along the line or at intervals, for example, every 2 m.

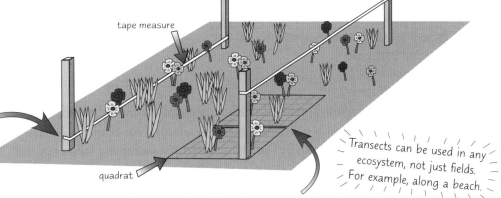

tape measure

quadrat

Transects can be used in any ecosystem, not just fields. For example, along a beach.

When Collecting Environmental Data You Need to Think About...

① Reliability

1) Quadrats and transects are pretty good tools for finding out how an organism is distributed.

2) But, you have to work hard to make sure your results are reliable — which means making sure they are repeatable and reproducible (see page 2).

3) To make your results more reliable you need to take a large sample size, e.g. use as many quadrats and transects as possible in your sample area. Bigger samples are more representative of the whole population.

② Validity

1) For your results to be valid they must be reliable (see above) and answer the original question.

2) To answer the original question, you need to control all the variables.

3) The question you want to answer is whether a difference in distribution between two sample areas is due to a difference in one environmental factor.

4) If you've controlled all the other variables that could be affecting the distribution, you'll know whether a difference in distribution is caused by the environmental factor or not.

5) If you don't control the other variables you won't know whether any correlation you've found is because of chance, because of the environmental factor you're looking at or because of a different variable — the study won't give you valid data.

6) Use random samples, e.g. randomly put down or mark out your quadrat or transect. If all your samples are in one spot, and everywhere else is different, the results you get won't be valid.

A slug that's been run over — definitely a widely-spread organism...

In the exam, you may get the results of a study into the distribution of organisms and be asked questions on it. If you need to work out the number of organisms per transect just take your time and check your answer. If you're asked about reliability, read the method carefully and think about the sample size and random samples.

Revision Summary for Biology 2a

And where do you think you're going? It's no use just reading through and thinking you've got it all — this stuff will only stick in your head if you've learnt it <u>properly</u>. And that's what these questions are for.
I won't pretend they'll be easy — they're not meant to be, but all the information's in the section somewhere.
Have a go at all the questions, then if there are any you can't answer, go back, look stuff up and try again.
Enjoy...

1) Name five parts of a cell that both plant and animal cells have. What three things do plant cells have that animal cells don't?
2) Where is the genetic material found in:
   a) bacterial cells
   b) animal cells?
3) What is diffusion?
4) Name three substances that can diffuse through cell membranes, and two that can't.
5) Give three ways that a palisade leaf cell is adapted for photosynthesis.
6) Give three ways that a sperm cell is adapted for swimming to an egg cell.
7) What is a tissue? What is an organ?
8) Give three examples of tissues in the human stomach, and say what job they do.
9) Name one organ system found in the human body.
10) Give an example of a plant tissue and a plant organ.
11) Write down the equation for photosynthesis.
12) What is the green substance in leaves that absorbs sunlight?
13) Name the three factors that can limit the rate of photosynthesis.
14) You carry out an experiment where you change the light intensity experienced by a piece of Canadian pondweed by changing the distance between the pondweed and a lamp supplying it with light.
    Write down three important things which must be kept constant for this experiment to be a fair test.
15) Explain why it's important that a plant doesn't get too hot.
16) Describe three things that a gardener could do to make sure she grows a good crop of tomatoes in her greenhouse.
17) Why is glucose turned into starch when plants need to store it for later?
18) Write down four other ways that plants can use the glucose produced by photosynthesis.
19) What is a habitat?
20) Give five environmental factors that can affect the distribution of organisms.
21) Briefly describe how you could find out how common an organism is in two sample areas using quadrats.
22) Describe one way of using a transect to find out how an organism is distributed across an area.

Enzymes

Chemical reactions are what make you work. And enzymes are what make them work.

Enzymes Are Catalysts Produced by Living Things

1) Living things have thousands of different chemical reactions going on inside them all the time. These reactions need to be carefully controlled — to get the right amounts of substances.

2) You can usually make a reaction happen more quickly by raising the temperature. This would speed up the useful reactions but also the unwanted ones too... not good. There's also a limit to how far you can raise the temperature inside a living creature before its cells start getting damaged.

3) So... living things produce enzymes that act as biological catalysts. Enzymes reduce the need for high temperatures and we only have enzymes to speed up the useful chemical reactions in the body.

> A CATALYST is a substance which INCREASES the speed of a reaction,
> without being CHANGED or USED UP in the reaction.

4) Enzymes are all proteins and all proteins are made up of chains of amino acids. These chains are folded into unique shapes, which enzymes need to do their jobs (see below).

5) As well as catalysts, proteins act as structural components of tissues (e.g. muscles), hormones and antibodies.

Enzymes Have Special Shapes So They Can Catalyse Reactions

1) Chemical reactions usually involve things either being split apart or joined together.

2) Every enzyme has a unique shape that fits onto the substance involved in a reaction.

3) Enzymes are really picky — they usually only catalyse one reaction.

4) This is because, for the enzyme to work, the substance has to fit its special shape. If the substance doesn't match the enzyme's shape, then the reaction won't be catalysed.

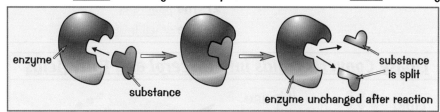

Enzymes Need the Right Temperature and pH

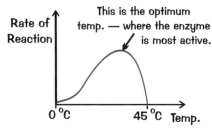

This is the optimum temp. — where the enzyme is most active.

Rate of Reaction

0 °C   45 °C Temp.

1) Changing the temperature changes the rate of an enzyme-catalysed reaction.

2) Like with any reaction, a higher temperature increases the rate at first. But if it gets too hot, some of the bonds holding the enzyme together break. This destroys the enzyme's special shape and so it won't work any more. It's said to be denatured.

3) Enzymes in the human body normally work best at around 37 °C.

4) The pH also affects enzymes. If it's too high or too low, the pH interferes with the bonds holding the enzyme together. This changes the shape and denatures the enzyme.

5) All enzymes have an optimum pH that they work best at. It's often neutral pH 7, but not always — e.g. pepsin is an enzyme used to break down proteins in the stomach. It works best at pH 2, which means it's well-suited to the acidic conditions there.

Rate of reaction   Optimum pH

pH

If only enzymes could speed up revision...

Just like you've got to have the correct key for a lock, you've got to have the right substance for an enzyme. If the substance doesn't fit, the enzyme won't catalyse the reaction...

Enzymes and Digestion

Not all enzymes work inside body cells — some work <u>outside</u> cells. For example, the enzymes used in <u>digestion</u> are produced by cells and then <u>released</u> into the <u>gut</u> to <u>mix</u> with <u>food</u>. Makes sense, really.

Digestive Enzymes Break Down Big Molecules into Smaller Ones

1) <u>Starch</u>, <u>proteins</u> and <u>fats</u> are BIG molecules.
   They're too big to pass through the walls of the digestive system.

2) <u>Sugars</u>, <u>amino acids</u>, <u>glycerol</u> and <u>fatty acids</u> are much smaller molecules.
   They can pass easily through the walls of the digestive system.

3) The <u>digestive enzymes</u> break down the BIG molecules into the smaller ones.

Amylase Converts Starch into Sugars

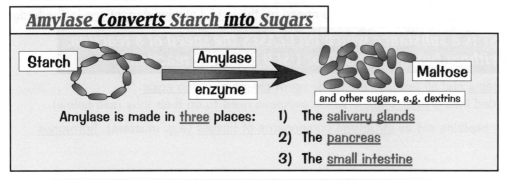

Amylase is made in <u>three</u> places: 1) The <u>salivary glands</u>
2) The <u>pancreas</u>
3) The <u>small intestine</u>

Protease Converts Proteins into Amino Acids

Protease is made in <u>three</u> places: 1) The <u>stomach</u> (it's called <u>pepsin</u> there)
2) The <u>pancreas</u>
3) The <u>small intestine</u>

Lipase Converts Lipids into Glycerol and Fatty Acids

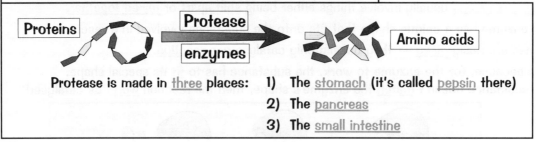

Lipase is made in <u>two</u> places: 1) The <u>pancreas</u>
2) The <u>small intestine</u>

Remember, lipids are fats and oils.

Bile Neutralises the Stomach Acid and Emulsifies Fats

1) Bile is <u>produced</u> in the <u>liver</u>. It's <u>stored</u> in the <u>gall bladder</u> before it's released into the <u>small intestine</u>.

2) The <u>hydrochloric acid</u> in the stomach makes the pH <u>too acidic</u> for enzymes in the small intestine to work properly. Bile is <u>alkaline</u> — it <u>neutralises</u> the acid and makes conditions <u>alkaline</u>. The enzymes in the small intestine <u>work best</u> in these alkaline conditions.

3) It <u>emulsifies</u> fats. In other words it breaks the fat into <u>tiny droplets</u>. This gives a much <u>bigger surface area</u> of fat for the enzyme lipase to work on — which makes its digestion <u>faster</u>.

What do you call an acid that's eaten all the pies...

This all happens inside our digestive system, but there are some microorganisms that secrete their digestive enzymes <u>outside their body</u> onto the food. The food's digested, then the microorganism absorbs the nutrients. Nice. I wouldn't like to empty the contents of my stomach onto my plate before eating it.

More on Enzymes and Digestion

So now you know what the enzymes do, here's a nice big picture of the whole of the digestive system.

The Breakdown of Food is Catalysed by Enzymes

1) Enzymes used in the digestive system are produced by specialised cells in glands and in the gut lining.
2) Different enzymes catalyse the breakdown of different food molecules.

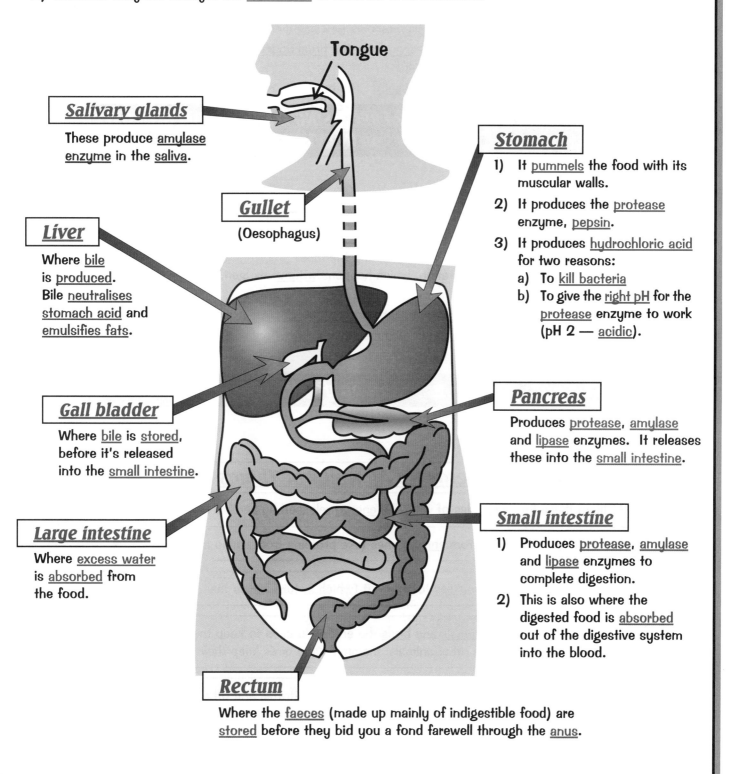

Tongue

Salivary glands
These produce amylase enzyme in the saliva.

Gullet
(Oesophagus)

Liver
Where bile is produced. Bile neutralises stomach acid and emulsifies fats.

Gall bladder
Where bile is stored, before it's released into the small intestine.

Large intestine
Where excess water is absorbed from the food.

Rectum
Where the faeces (made up mainly of indigestible food) are stored before they bid you a fond farewell through the anus.

Stomach
1) It pummels the food with its muscular walls.
2) It produces the protease enzyme, pepsin.
3) It produces hydrochloric acid for two reasons:
   a) To kill bacteria
   b) To give the right pH for the protease enzyme to work (pH 2 — acidic).

Pancreas
Produces protease, amylase and lipase enzymes. It releases these into the small intestine.

Small intestine
1) Produces protease, amylase and lipase enzymes to complete digestion.
2) This is also where the digested food is absorbed out of the digestive system into the blood.

Mmmm — so who's for a chocolate digestive...

Did you know that the whole of your digestive system is actually a hole that goes right through your body. Think about it. It just gets loads of food, digestive juices and enzymes piled into it. Most of it's then absorbed into the body and the rest is politely stored ready for removal.

Enzymes and Respiration

Many chemical reactions inside cells are controlled by enzymes — including the ones in respiration.

Respiration is NOT "Breathing In and Out"

Respiration involves many reactions, all of which are catalysed by enzymes.
These are really important reactions, as respiration releases the energy
that the cell needs to do just about everything.

1) Respiration is not breathing in and breathing out, as you might think.
2) Respiration is the process of releasing energy from the breakdown of glucose
   — and it goes on in every cell in your body.
3) It happens in plants too. All living things respire. It's how they release energy from their food.

> **RESPIRATION is the process of RELEASING ENERGY FROM GLUCOSE,
> which goes on IN EVERY CELL**

Aerobic Respiration Needs Plenty of Oxygen

1) Aerobic respiration is respiration using oxygen. It's the most efficient way to release energy from glucose. (You can also have anaerobic respiration, which happens without oxygen, but that doesn't release nearly as much energy — see page 25.)
2) Aerobic respiration goes on all the time in plants and animals.
3) Most of the reactions in aerobic respiration happen inside mitochondria (see page 10).
4) You need to learn the overall word equation:

> **Glucose + oxygen $\Longrightarrow$ carbon dioxide + water + ENERGY**

Respiration Releases Energy for All Kinds of Things

You need to learn these four examples of what the energy released by aerobic respiration is used for:

1) To build up larger molecules from smaller ones (like proteins from amino acids).

2) In animals, to allow the muscles to contract (which in turn allows them to move about).

3) In mammals and birds the energy is used to keep their body temperature steady (unlike other animals, mammals and birds keep their bodies constantly warm).

4) In plants, to build sugars, nitrates and other nutrients into amino acids, which are then built up into proteins.

Breathe, 2, 3, 4 — and release, 6, 7, 8...

So... respiration — that's a pretty important thing. Cyanide is a really nasty toxin that stops respiration by stopping enzymes involved in the process from working — so it's pretty poisonous (it can kill you).
Your brain, heart and liver are affected first because they have the highest energy demands... nice.

Exercise

When you exercise, your body quickly adapts so that your muscles get <u>more oxygen and glucose</u> to supply <u>energy</u>. If your body can't get enough oxygen or glucose to them, it has some back-up plans ready.

Exercise Increases the Heart Rate

1) Muscles are made of <u>muscle cells</u>. These use <u>oxygen</u> to <u>release energy</u> from <u>glucose</u> (<u>aerobic respiration</u> — see page 24), which is used to <u>contract</u> the muscles.

2) An <u>increase</u> in muscle activity requires <u>more glucose and oxygen</u> to be supplied to the muscle cells. Extra carbon dioxide needs to be <u>removed</u> from the muscle cells. For this to happen the blood has to flow at a <u>faster</u> rate.

3) This is why physical activity:
   - <u>increases</u> your <u>breathing rate</u> and makes you breathe <u>more deeply</u> to meet the demand for <u>extra oxygen</u>.
   - <u>increases</u> the speed at which the <u>heart pumps</u>.

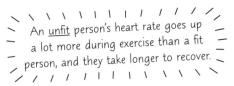
An <u>unfit</u> person's heart rate goes up a lot more during exercise than a fit person, and they take longer to recover.

Glycogen is Used During Exercise

1) Some <u>glucose</u> from food is <u>stored</u> as <u>glycogen</u>.

2) Glycogen's mainly stored in the liver, but each <u>muscle</u> also has its own store.

3) During vigorous exercise muscles use glucose <u>rapidly</u>, so some of the stored glycogen is converted back to <u>glucose</u> to provide more energy.

Anaerobic Respiration is Used if There's Not Enough Oxygen

1) When you do vigorous exercise and your body can't supply enough <u>oxygen</u> to your muscles, they start doing <u>anaerobic respiration</u> instead of aerobic respiration.

2) "Anaerobic" just means "<u>without</u> oxygen". It's the <u>incomplete</u> breakdown of glucose, which produces <u>lactic acid</u>.

 glucose → energy + lactic acid

3) This is <u>**NOT the best way to convert glucose into energy**</u> because <u>lactic acid</u> builds up in the muscles, which gets <u>painful</u>. It also causes <u>muscle fatigue</u> — the muscles get <u>tired</u> and they <u>stop contracting efficiently</u>.

4) Another downside is that <u>anaerobic respiration</u> does <u>not release nearly as much energy</u> as aerobic respiration — but it's useful in emergencies.

5) The <u>advantage</u> is that at least you can keep on using your muscles for a while longer.

Anaerobic Respiration Leads to an Oxygen Debt

1) After resorting to anaerobic respiration, when you stop exercising you'll have an "<u>oxygen debt</u>".

2) In other words you have to "<u>repay</u>" the oxygen that you didn't get to your muscles in time, because your <u>lungs</u>, <u>heart</u> and <u>blood</u> couldn't keep up with the <u>demand</u> earlier on.

3) This means you have to keep breathing hard for a while <u>after you stop</u>, to get <u>more oxygen</u> into your blood. Blood flows through your muscles to <u>remove</u> the lactic acid by <u>oxidising</u> it to harmless CO_2 and water.

4) While <u>high levels</u> of <u>CO_2</u> and <u>lactic acid</u> are detected in the blood (by the brain), the <u>pulse</u> and <u>breathing rate</u> stay high to try and rectify the situation.

Oxygen debt — cheap to pay back...

Phew... bet you're exhausted after reading this. Still, it needs learning before you have a pit stop. In the exam, you could be asked to <u>interpret data</u> on the <u>effects of exercise</u> on the body — so make sure you <u>know this page</u>.

Uses of Enzymes

Some microorganisms produce enzymes which pass out of their cells and catalyse reactions outside them (e.g. to digest the microorganism's food). These enzymes have many uses in the home and in industry.

Enzymes Are Used in Biological Detergents

1) Enzymes are the 'biological' ingredients in biological detergents and washing powders.

2) They're mainly protein-digesting enzymes (proteases) and fat-digesting enzymes (lipases).

3) Because the enzymes break down animal and plant matter, they're ideal for removing stains like food or blood.

4) Biological detergents are also more effective at working at low temperatures (e.g. 30 °C) than other types of detergents.

Enzymes Are Used to Change Foods

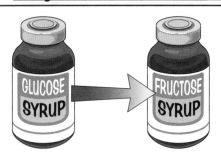

1) The proteins in some baby foods are 'pre-digested' using protein-digesting enzymes (proteases), so they're easier for the baby to digest.

2) Carbohydrate-digesting enzymes (carbohydrases) can be used to turn starch syrup (yuk) into sugar syrup (yum).

3) Glucose syrup can be turned into fructose syrup using an isomerase enzyme. Fructose is sweeter, so you can use less of it — good for slimming foods and drinks.

Using Enzymes in Industry Takes a Lot of Control

Enzymes are really useful in industry. They speed up reactions without the need for high temperatures and pressures. You need to know the advantages and disadvantages of using them, so here are a few to get you started:

ADVANTAGES

1) They're specific, so they only catalyse the reaction you want them to.
2) Using lower temperatures and pressures means a lower cost as it saves energy.
3) Enzymes work for a long time, so after the initial cost of buying them, you can continually use them.
4) They are biodegradable and therefore cause less environmental pollution.

DISADVANTAGES

1) Some people can develop allergies to the enzymes (e.g. in biological washing powders).
2) Enzymes can be denatured by even a small increase in temperature. They're also susceptible to poisons and changes in pH. This means the conditions in which they work must be tightly controlled.
3) Enzymes can be expensive to produce.
4) Contamination of the enzyme with other substances can affect the reaction.

There's a lot to learn — but don't be deterred gents...

Enzymes are so picky. Even tiny little changes in pH or temperature will stop them working at maximum efficiency. They only catalyse one reaction as well, so you need to use a different one for each reaction. Temperamental little things these enzymes...

DNA

The first step in understanding genetics is getting to grips with DNA.

Chromosomes Are Really Long Molecules of DNA

1) <u>DNA</u> stands for <u>deoxyribonucleic acid</u>.
2) It contains all the <u>instructions</u> to put an organism together and <u>make it work</u>.
3) It's found in the <u>nucleus</u> of animal and plant cells, in really <u>long molecules</u> called <u>chromosomes</u>.

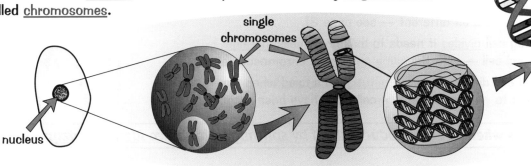

A DNA molecule with a double helix structure.

single chromosomes

nucleus

A Gene Codes for a Specific Protein

1) A <u>gene</u> is a <u>section</u> of DNA. It contains the <u>instructions</u> to make a <u>specific protein</u>.
2) Cells make <u>proteins</u> by stringing <u>amino acids</u> together in a particular order.
3) Only <u>20</u> amino acids are used, but they make up <u>thousands</u> of different <u>proteins</u>.
4) Genes simply tell cells <u>in what order</u> to put the amino acids together.
5) DNA also determines what <u>proteins</u> the cell <u>produces</u>, e.g. haemoglobin, keratin.
6) That in turn determines what <u>type of cell</u> it is, e.g. red blood cell, skin cell.

Everyone has Unique DNA...   ...except identical twins and clones

Almost everyone's DNA is <u>unique</u>. The only exceptions are <u>identical twins</u>, where the two people have identical DNA, and <u>clones</u>.

<u>DNA fingerprinting</u> (or genetic fingerprinting) is a way of <u>cutting up</u> a person's DNA into small sections and then <u>separating</u> them. Every person's genetic fingerprint has a <u>unique</u> pattern (unless they're identical twins or clones of course). This means you can <u>tell people apart</u> by <u>comparing samples</u> of their DNA.

DNA fingerprinting is used in...

DNA from crime scene   suspect 1   suspect 2   suspect 3

1) <u>Forensic science</u> — DNA (from hair, skin flakes, blood, semen etc.) taken from a <u>crime scene</u> is compared with a DNA sample taken from a suspect. In the diagram, suspect 1's DNA has the same pattern as the DNA from the crime scene — so suspect 1 was probably at the crime scene.
2) <u>Paternity testing</u> — to see if a man is the father of a particular child.

Some people would like there to be a national <u>genetic database</u> of everyone in the country. That way, DNA from a crime scene could be checked against <u>everyone</u> in the country to see whose it was. But others think this is a big <u>invasion of privacy</u>, and they worry about how <u>safe</u> the data would be and what <u>else</u> it might be used for. There are also <u>scientific problems</u> — <u>false positives</u> can occur if <u>errors</u> are made in the procedure or if the data is <u>misinterpreted</u>.

So the trick is — frame your twin and they'll never get you...

In the exam you might have to interpret data on <u>DNA fingerprinting for identification</u>. They could give you the results of a <u>paternity test</u> — the DNA fingerprint of a child, their mother and some possible fathers. Remember, <u>half</u> of the child's DNA fingerprint will <u>match</u> the <u>mother's DNA</u> fingerprint and <u>half</u> will match the <u>actual father's</u>.

Cell Division — Mitosis

In order to <u>survive</u> and <u>grow</u>, our cells have got to be able to <u>divide</u>. And that means our <u>DNA</u> as well...

Mitosis Makes New Cells for Growth and Repair

1) <u>Body cells</u> normally have <u>two copies</u> of each <u>chromosome</u> — one from the organism's '<u>mother</u>', and one from its '<u>father</u>'. So, humans have two copies of chromosome 1, two copies of chromosome 2, etc.

2) The diagram shows the <u>23 pairs of chromosomes</u> from a human cell. The 23rd pair are a bit different — see page 31.

3) When a body cell <u>divides</u> it needs to make new cells <u>identical</u> to the <u>original</u> cell — with the <u>same number</u> of chromosomes.

4) This type of cell division is called <u>mitosis</u>. It's used when plants and animals want to <u>grow</u> or to <u>replace</u> cells that have been <u>damaged</u>.

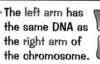

> "<u>MITOSIS</u> is when a cell reproduces itself <u>by splitting</u> to form <u>two identical offspring</u>."

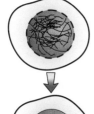

In a cell that's not dividing, the DNA is all spread out in <u>long strings</u>.

If the cell gets a signal to <u>divide</u>, it needs to <u>duplicate</u> its DNA — so there's one copy for each new cell. The DNA is copied and forms <u>X-shaped</u> chromosomes. Each 'arm' of the chromosome is an <u>exact duplicate</u> of the other.

The left arm has the same DNA as the right arm of the chromosome.

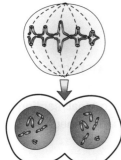

The chromosomes then <u>line up</u> at the centre of the cell and <u>cell fibres</u> pull them apart. The <u>two arms</u> of each chromosome go to <u>opposite ends</u> of the cell.

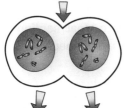

<u>Membranes</u> form around each of the sets of chromosomes. These become the <u>nuclei</u> of the two new cells.

Lastly, the <u>cytoplasm</u> divides.

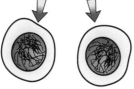

You now have <u>two new cells</u> containing exactly the same DNA — they're <u>identical</u>.

Asexual Reproduction Also Uses Mitosis

1) Some organisms also <u>reproduce</u> by mitosis, e.g. strawberry plants form runners in this way, which become new plants.

2) This is an example of <u>asexual</u> reproduction.

3) The offspring have exactly the <u>same genes</u> as the parent — so there's <u>no variation</u>.

A cell's favourite computer game — divide and conquer...

This can seem tricky at first. But <u>don't worry</u> — just go through it <u>slowly</u>, one step at a time. This type of division produces <u>identical cells</u>, but there's another type which doesn't... (see next page)

Cell Division — Meiosis

You thought mitosis was exciting. Hah. You ain't seen nothing yet...

Gametes Have Half the Usual Number of Chromosomes

1) During sexual reproduction, two cells called gametes (sex cells) combine to form a new individual.

2) Gametes only have one copy of each chromosome. This is so that you can combine one sex cell from the 'mother' and one sex cell from the 'father' and still end up with the right number of chromosomes in body cells. For example, human body cells have 46 chromosomes. The gametes have 23 chromosomes each, so that when an egg and sperm combine, you get 46 chromosomes again.

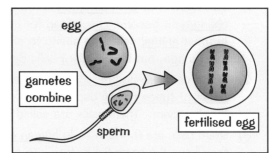

egg

gametes combine

sperm

fertilised egg

3) The new individual will have a mixture of two sets of chromosomes, so it will inherit features from both parents. This is how sexual reproduction produces variation.

Meiosis Involves Two Divisions

To make new cells which only have half the original number of chromosomes, cells divide by meiosis. In humans, it only happens in the reproductive organs (e.g. ovaries and testes).

"MEIOSIS produces cells which have half the normal number of chromosomes."

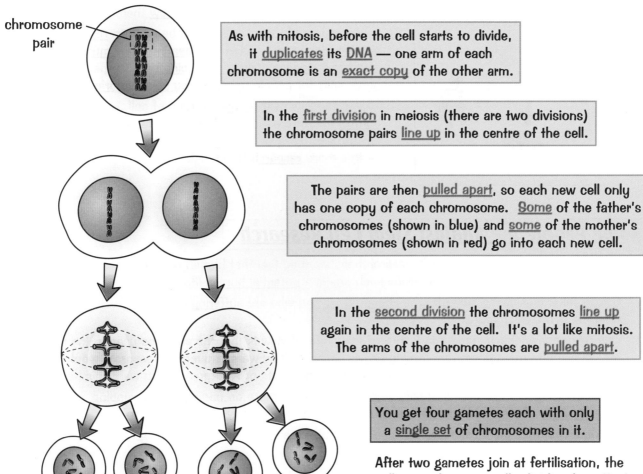

chromosome pair

As with mitosis, before the cell starts to divide, it duplicates its DNA — one arm of each chromosome is an exact copy of the other arm.

In the first division in meiosis (there are two divisions) the chromosome pairs line up in the centre of the cell.

The pairs are then pulled apart, so each new cell only has one copy of each chromosome. Some of the father's chromosomes (shown in blue) and some of the mother's chromosomes (shown in red) go into each new cell.

In the second division the chromosomes line up again in the centre of the cell. It's a lot like mitosis. The arms of the chromosomes are pulled apart.

You get four gametes each with only a single set of chromosomes in it.

After two gametes join at fertilisation, the cell grows by repeatedly dividing by mitosis.

Now that I have your undivided attention...

Remember, in humans, meiosis only occurs in reproductive organs where gametes are being made.

Stem Cells

Stem cell research has exciting possibilities, but it's also pretty controversial.

Embryonic Stem Cells Can Turn into ANY Type of Cell

1) You know that <u>differentiation</u> is the process by which a cell <u>changes</u> to become <u>specialised</u> for its job (see page 12). In most <u>animal</u> cells, the ability to differentiate is <u>lost</u> at an early stage, but lots of <u>plant</u> cells <u>don't</u> ever lose this ability.

2) Some cells are <u>undifferentiated</u>. They can develop into <u>different types of cell</u> depending on what <u>instructions</u> they're given. These cells are called <u>STEM CELLS</u>.

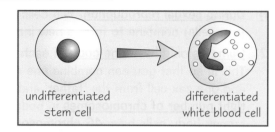
undifferentiated stem cell — differentiated white blood cell

3) Stem cells are found in early <u>human embryos</u>. They're <u>exciting</u> to doctors and medical researchers because they have the potential to turn into <u>any</u> kind of cell at all. This makes sense if you think about it — <u>all</u> the <u>different types</u> of cell found in a human being have to come from those <u>few cells</u> in the early embryo.

4) Adults also have stem cells, but they're only found in certain places, like <u>bone marrow</u>. These aren't as <u>versatile</u> as embryonic stem cells — they can't turn into <u>any</u> cell type at all, only certain ones.

Stem Cells May Be Able to Cure Many Diseases

1) Medicine <u>already</u> uses adult stem cells to cure <u>disease</u>. For example, people with some <u>blood diseases</u> (e.g. <u>sickle cell anaemia</u>) can be treated by <u>bone marrow transplants</u>. Bone marrow contains <u>stem cells</u> that can turn into <u>new blood cells</u> to replace the faulty old ones.

2) Scientists can also <u>extract</u> stem cells from very early human embryos and <u>grow</u> them.

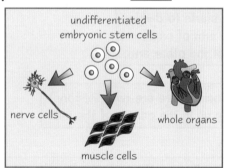
undifferentiated embryonic stem cells
nerve cells
whole organs
muscle cells

3) These embryonic stem cells could be used to <u>replace faulty cells</u> in sick people — you could make <u>beating heart muscle cells</u> for people with <u>heart disease</u>, <u>insulin-producing cells</u> for people with <u>diabetes</u>, <u>nerve cells</u> for people <u>paralysed by spinal injuries</u>, and so on.

4) To get cultures of <u>one specific type</u> of cell, researchers try to <u>control</u> the differentiation of the stem cells by changing the environment they're growing in. So far, it's still a bit hit and miss — lots more <u>research</u> is needed.

Some People Are Against Stem Cell Research

1) Some people are <u>against</u> stem cell research because they feel that human embryos <u>shouldn't</u> be used for experiments since each one is a <u>potential human life</u>.

2) Others think that curing patients who <u>already exist</u> and who are <u>suffering</u> is more important than the rights of <u>embryos</u>.

3) One fairly convincing argument in favour of this point of view is that the embryos used in the research are usually <u>unwanted ones</u> from <u>fertility clinics</u> which, if they weren't used for research, would probably just be <u>destroyed</u>. But of course, campaigners for the rights of embryos usually want this banned too.

4) These campaigners feel that scientists should concentrate more on finding and developing <u>other sources</u> of stem cells, so people could be helped <u>without</u> having to use embryos.

5) In some countries stem cell research is <u>banned</u>, but it's allowed in the UK as long as it follows <u>strict guidelines</u>.

But florists cell stems, and nobody complains about that...

The potential of stem cells is huge — but it's early days yet. Research has recently been done into getting stem cells from <u>alternative sources</u>. For example, some researchers think it might be possible to get cells from <u>umbilical cords</u> to behave like embryonic stem cells.

X and Y Chromosomes

Now for a couple of very important little chromosomes...

Your Chromosomes Control Whether You're Male or Female

There are <u>22 matched pairs</u> of <u>chromosomes</u> in every human body cell. The <u>23rd pair</u> are labelled <u>XX</u> or <u>XY</u>. They're the two chromosomes that decide whether you turn out <u>male</u> or <u>female</u>.

> All <u>men</u> have an <u>X</u> and a <u>Y</u> chromosome: XY
> The <u>Y</u> chromosome causes <u>male characteristics</u>.
>
> All <u>women</u> have <u>two X</u> chromosomes: XX
> The <u>XX combination</u> allows <u>female characteristics</u> to develop.

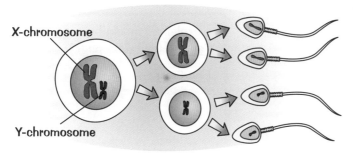

X-chromosome

Y-chromosome

When making sperm, the X and Y chromosomes are drawn apart in the first division in meiosis. There's a <u>50% chance</u> each sperm cell gets an <u>X-chromosome</u> and a <u>50% chance</u> it gets a <u>Y-chromosome</u>.

A similar thing happens when making eggs. But the original cell has two X-chromosomes, so all the eggs have one X-chromosome.

Genetic Diagrams Show the Possible Combinations of Gametes

1) To find the <u>probability</u> of getting a boy or a girl, you can draw a <u>genetic diagram</u>.

2) Put the <u>possible gametes</u> from <u>one</u> parent down the side, and those from the <u>other</u> parent along the top.

3) Then in each middle square you <u>fill in</u> the letters from the top and side that line up with that square. The <u>pairs of letters</u> in the middle show the possible combinations of the gametes.

4) There are <u>two XX results</u> and <u>two XY results</u>, so there's the same probability of getting a boy or a girl.

5) Don't forget that this <u>50:50 ratio</u> is only a <u>probability</u> at each pregnancy. If you had four kids they <u>could</u> all be <u>boys</u> — yes I know, terrifying isn't it?

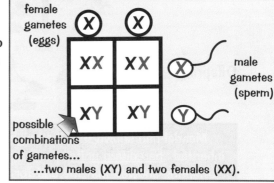

female gametes (eggs)

male gametes (sperm)

possible combinations of gametes...
...two males (XY) and two females (XX).

The other type of genetic diagram looks a bit more complicated, but it shows exactly the same thing.

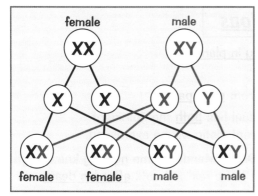

female — female — male — male

1) At the top are the <u>parents</u>.

2) The middle circles show the <u>possible gametes</u> that are formed. One gamete from the female combines with one gamete from the male (during fertilisation).

3) The criss-cross lines show <u>all</u> the <u>possible</u> ways the X and Y chromosomes <u>could</u> combine. The <u>possible combinations</u> of the offspring are shown in the bottom circles.

4) Remember, only <u>one</u> of these possibilities would <u>actually happen</u> for any one offspring.

Have you got the Y-factor...

Most genetic diagrams you'll see in exams concentrate on a <u>gene</u>, instead of a <u>chromosome</u>. But the principle's the same. Don't worry — there are loads of other examples on the following pages.

The Work of Mendel

Some people forget about Mendel but I reckon he's the <u>Granddaddy of Genetics</u>. Here's a whole page on him.

Mendel <u>Did</u> Genetic Experiments <u>with</u> Pea Plants

<u>Gregor Mendel</u> was an Austrian monk who trained in <u>mathematics</u> and <u>natural history</u> at the University of Vienna. On his garden plot at the monastery, Mendel noted how <u>characteristics</u> in <u>plants</u> were <u>passed on</u> from one generation to the next.

The results of his research were published in <u>1866</u> and eventually became the <u>foundation</u> of modern <u>genetics</u>.

The diagrams show two <u>crosses for height</u> in <u>pea plants</u> that Mendel carried out...

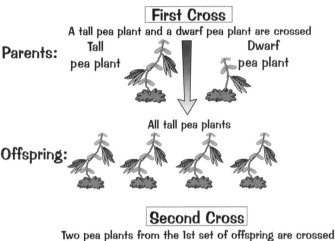

First Cross

A tall pea plant and a dwarf pea plant are crossed

Parents: Tall pea plant — Dwarf pea plant

All tall pea plants

Offspring:

Second Cross

Two pea plants from the 1st set of offspring are crossed

Parents: Tall pea plant — Tall pea plant

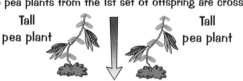

Three tall pea plants and one dwarf pea plant

Offspring:

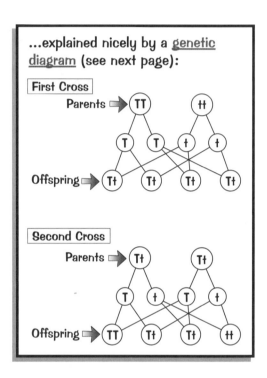

...explained nicely by a <u>genetic diagram</u> (see next page):

First Cross

Parents → TT   tt

T T t t

Offspring → Tt Tt Tt Tt

Second Cross

Parents → Tt   Tt

T t T t

Offspring → TT Tt Tt tt

> Mendel had shown that the height characteristic in pea plants was determined by separately inherited "<u>hereditary units</u>" passed on from each parent. The ratios of tall and dwarf plants in the offspring showed that the unit for tall plants, <u>T</u>, was <u>dominant</u> over the unit for dwarf plants, <u>t</u>.

Mendel Reached <u>Three Important Conclusions</u>

Mendel reached these three important conclusions about <u>heredity in plants</u>:

1) Characteristics in plants are determined by "<u>hereditary units</u>".

2) Hereditary units are passed on from both parents, <u>one unit</u> from <u>each parent</u>.

3) Hereditary units can be <u>dominant</u> or <u>recessive</u> — if an individual has <u>both</u> the dominant and the recessive unit for a characteristic, the <u>dominant</u> characteristic will be expressed.

We now know that the "hereditary units" are of course <u>genes</u>. But in Mendel's time <u>nobody</u> knew anything about genes or DNA, and so the <u>significance</u> of his work was not to be realised until <u>after his death</u>.

Clearly, being a monk in the 1800s was a right laugh...

Well, there was no TV in those days, you see. Monks had to make their <u>own entertainment</u>. And in Mendel's case, that involved growing lots and lots of <u>peas</u>. He was a very clever lad, was Mendel, but unfortunately just a bit <u>ahead of his time</u>. Nobody had a clue what he was going on about.

Genetic Diagrams

In the exam they could ask you about the inheritance of any kind of characteristic that's controlled by a single gene, because the principle's always the same. So here's a slightly bizarre example, to show you the basics.

Genetic Diagrams Show the Possible Genes of Offspring

1) Alleles are different versions of the same gene.

2) In genetic diagrams letters are usually used to represent alleles.

3) If an organism has two alleles for a particular gene the same, then it's homozygous. If its two alleles for a particular gene are different, then it's heterozygous.

4) If the two alleles are different, only one can determine what characteristic is present. The allele for the characteristic that's shown is called the dominant allele (use a capital letter for dominant alleles — e.g. 'C'). The other one is called recessive (and you show these with small letters — e.g. 'c').

5) For an organism to display a recessive characteristic, both its alleles must be recessive (e.g. cc). But to display a dominant characteristic the organism can be either CC or Cc, because the dominant allele overrules the recessive one if the plant/animal/other organism is heterozygous.

Remember, gametes only have one allele, but all the other cells in an organism have two.

Suppose You Find Yourself Cross-Breeding Crazy Hamsters...

Let's say that the gene which causes the crazy nature is recessive, so we use a small "b" for it, whilst normal (boring) behaviour is due to a dominant gene, so we represent it with a capital "B".

1) A crazy hamster must have the genotype bb. However, a normal hamster could have two possible genotypes — BB or Bb.

Genotype means what alleles you have. Phenotype means the actual characteristic.

2) Here's what happens if you breed from two homozygous hamsters:

Parents' phenotypes:	Normal	Crazy

Parents' genotypes: **BB** **bb**

Gametes' genotypes: B B b b

Offspring's genotypes: Bb Bb Bb Bb

Offspring's phenotypes: **All the offspring are normal (boring).**

3) If two of these offspring now breed, you'll get the next generation:

Parents' phenotypes: Normal Normal

Parents' genotypes: **Bb** **Bb**

Gametes' genotypes: B b B b

Offspring's genotypes: **BB** **Bb** **Bb** **bb**

Offspring's phenotypes: Normal Normal Normal Crazy!

When you cross two parents to look at just one characteristic, it's called a monohybrid cross.

4) This gives a 3:1 ratio of normal to crazy offspring in this generation. Remember that "results" like this are only probabilities — they don't say definitely what'll happen. (most likely, you'll end up trying to contain a mini-riot of nine lunatic baby hamsters.)

What do you get if you cross a kangaroo and a sheep...

...a ratio of 1:1 kangsheep to sheeparoos... bet you thought I was going to say a woolly jumper. In the exam you might be given the results of a breeding experiment and asked to say whether a characteristic is dominant or recessive. To figure it out, look at the ratios of the characteristic in different generations — just like in the diagrams. And remember that a 3:1 ratio of normal:crazy gives a 1 in 4 or 25% probability of being crazy.

Genetic Disorders

It's not just characteristics that are passed on — some <u>disorders</u> are inherited. You need to <u>learn these two</u>.

Cystic Fibrosis <u>is Caused by a Recessive Allele</u>

<u>Cystic fibrosis</u> is a <u>genetic disorder</u> of the <u>cell membranes</u>. It <u>results</u> in the body producing a lot of thick sticky <u>mucus</u> in the <u>air passages</u> and in the <u>pancreas</u>.

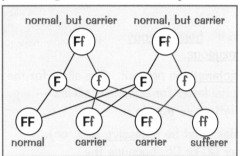

normal, but carrier   normal, but carrier

Ff   Ff

F   f   F   f

FF   Ff   Ff   ff

normal   carrier   carrier   sufferer

1) The allele which causes cystic fibrosis is a <u>recessive allele</u>, 'f', carried by about <u>1 person in 25</u>.

2) Because it's recessive, people with only <u>one copy</u> of the allele <u>won't</u> have the disorder — they're known as <u>carriers</u>.

3) For a child to have the disorder, <u>both parents</u> must be either <u>carriers</u> or <u>sufferers</u>.

4) As the diagram shows there's a <u>1 in 4 chance</u> of a child having the disorder if <u>both</u> parents are <u>carriers</u>.

Polydactyly <u>is Caused by a Dominant Allele</u>

<u>Polydactyly</u> is a <u>genetic disorder</u> where a baby's born with <u>extra fingers or toes</u>. It doesn't usually cause any other problems so <u>isn't life-threatening</u>.

1) The disorder is caused by a <u>dominant allele</u>, 'D', and so can be inherited if just <u>one parent</u> carries the defective allele.

2) The <u>parent</u> that <u>has</u> the defective allele will be a <u>sufferer</u> too since the allele is dominant.

3) As the genetic diagram shows, there's a <u>50% chance</u> of a child having the disorder if <u>one</u> parent has the D allele.

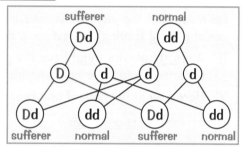

sufferer   normal

Dd   dd

D   d   d   d

Dd   dd   Dd   dd

sufferer   normal   sufferer   normal

Embryos <u>Can Be</u> Screened <u>for Genetic Disorders</u>

1) During <u>in vitro fertilisation</u> (IVF), embryos are fertilised in a <u>laboratory</u>, and then <u>implanted</u> into the mother's womb. <u>More</u> than one egg is fertilised, so there's a better chance of the IVF being <u>successful</u>.

2) Before being implanted, it's possible to <u>remove a cell</u> from each embryo and <u>analyse</u> its <u>genes</u>.

3) Many <u>genetic disorders</u> could be <u>detected</u> in this way, such as cystic fibrosis.

4) Embryos with '<u>good</u>' alleles would be <u>implanted</u> into the mother — the ones with '<u>bad</u>' alleles <u>destroyed</u>.

There is a <u>huge debate</u> raging about <u>embryonic screening</u>. Here are some arguments <u>for</u> and <u>against</u> it.

Against Embryonic Screening	For Embryonic Screening
1) There may come a point where everyone wants to screen their embryos so they can pick the most '<u>desirable</u>' one, e.g. they want a blue-eyed, blond-haired, intelligent boy.	1) It will help to stop people <u>suffering</u>.
2) The rejected embryos are <u>destroyed</u> — they could have developed into humans.	2) There are <u>laws</u> to stop it going too far. At the moment parents cannot even select the sex of their baby (unless it's for health reasons).
3) It implies that <u>people</u> with <u>genetic problems</u> are 'undesirable' — this could increase <u>prejudice</u>.	3) During IVF, most of the embryos are <u>destroyed</u> anyway — screening just allows the selected one to be <u>healthy</u>.
4) Screening is <u>expensive</u>.	4) Treating disorders costs the Government (and the taxpayers) a lot of <u>money</u>.

Many people think that embryonic screening <u>isn't justified</u> for genetic disorders that <u>don't</u> affect a person's health, such as <u>polydactyly</u>.

Embryonic screening — it's a tricky one...

In the exam you may be asked to <u>compare</u> the issues <u>for</u> and <u>against</u> embryonic screening for <u>different disorders</u>. So make sure you can apply the <u>pros</u> and <u>cons</u> listed above to different disorders and you'll be sorted.

More Genetic Diagrams

You've got to be able to <u>predict</u> and <u>explain</u> the outcomes of crosses between individuals for each <u>possible combination</u> of <u>dominant</u> and <u>recessive alleles</u> of a gene. You should be able to draw a <u>genetic diagram</u> and <u>work it out</u> — but it'll be easier if you've seen them all before. So here are a couple more examples for you. You also need to know how to interpret another type of genetic diagram called a <u>family tree</u>...

All the Offspring are Normal

Let's take another look at the <u>crazy hamster</u> example from page 33:

In this cross, a hamster with <u>two dominant alleles</u> (BB) is crossed with a hamster with <u>two recessive alleles</u> (bb). <u>All</u> the offspring are normal (boring).

But, if you crossed a hamster with <u>two dominant alleles</u> (BB) with a hamster with <u>a dominant</u> and <u>a recessive allele</u> (Bb), you would also get <u>all</u> normal (boring) offspring.

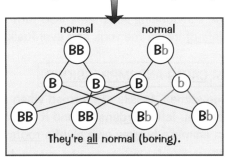

To find out <u>which</u> it was you'd have to <u>breed the offspring together</u> and see what kind of <u>ratio</u> you got that time — then you'd have a good idea. If it was <u>3:1</u>, it's likely that you originally had **BB** and bb.

There's a 1:1 Ratio in the Offspring

A cat with <u>long hair</u> was bred with another cat with <u>short hair</u>. The long hair is caused by a <u>dominant</u> allele 'H', and the short hair by a <u>recessive</u> allele 'h'.

They had 8 kittens — 4 with long hair and 4 with short hair.

This is a <u>1:1</u> ratio — it's what you'd expect when a parent with only <u>one dominant allele</u> (Hh) is crossed with a parent with <u>two recessive alleles</u> (hh).

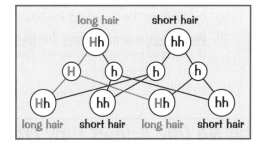

You Need to be Able to Interpret Family Trees

Knowing how inheritance works can help you to interpret a <u>family tree</u> — this is one for <u>cystic fibrosis</u>.

1) From the family tree, you can tell that the allele for cystic fibrosis <u>isn't</u> dominant because plenty of the family <u>carry</u> the allele but <u>aren't sufferers</u>.

2) There is a <u>25%</u> chance that the new baby will be a sufferer and a <u>50%</u> chance that it will be a carrier, as both of its parents are carriers but not sufferers. The case of the new baby is just the same as in the genetic diagram on page 34 — so the baby could be <u>normal</u> (FF), a <u>carrier</u> (Ff) or a <u>sufferer</u> (ff).

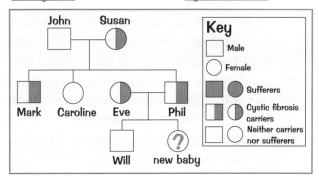

It's enough to make you go cross-eyed...

In the exam you might get a <u>family tree</u> showing the inheritance of a <u>dominant allele</u> — in this case there won't be any carriers shown. Also, remember that, a good way to work out a family tree is to write the <u>genotype</u> of each person onto it — you can practice by copying the family tree above and labelling the genotypes of everyone on it.

Fossils

Fossils are great. If they're <u>well-preserved</u>, you can see what oldy-worldy creatures <u>looked</u> like. They also show how living things have <u>evolved</u>. Although we're not sure how life started in the first place...

Fossils are the Remains of Plants and Animals

Fossils are the <u>remains</u> of organisms from <u>many years ago</u>, which are found in <u>rocks</u>.
Fossils provide the <u>evidence</u> that organisms lived ages ago. Fossils form in rocks in one of <u>three</u> ways:

1) FROM <u>GRADUAL REPLACEMENT</u> BY MINERALS   (Most fossils happen this way.)

1) Things like <u>teeth</u>, <u>shells</u>, <u>bones</u> etc., which <u>don't decay</u> easily, can last a long time when <u>buried</u>.

2) They're eventually <u>replaced by minerals</u> as they decay, forming a <u>rock-like substance</u> shaped like the original hard part.

3) The surrounding sediments also turn to rock, but the fossil stays <u>distinct</u> inside the rock and eventually someone <u>digs it up</u>.

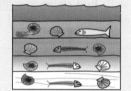

2) FROM <u>CASTS</u> AND <u>IMPRESSIONS</u>

1) Sometimes, fossils are formed when an organism is <u>buried</u> in a <u>soft</u> material like clay. The clay later <u>hardens</u> around it and the organism decays, leaving a <u>cast</u> of itself. An animal's <u>burrow</u> or a plant's <u>roots</u> can be preserved as casts.

2) Things like footprints can be <u>pressed</u> into these materials when soft, leaving an <u>impression</u> when it hardens.

3) FROM <u>PRESERVATION</u> IN PLACES WHERE NO DECAY HAPPENS

1) In <u>amber</u> (a clear yellow 'stone' made from fossilised resin) and <u>tar pits</u> there's no <u>oxygen</u> or <u>moisture</u> so <u>decay microbes</u> can't survive.

2) In <u>glaciers</u> it's too <u>cold</u> for the <u>decay microbes</u> to work.

3) <u>Peat bogs</u> are too <u>acidic</u> for <u>decay microbes</u>.
(A fully preserved man they named 'Pete Marsh' was found in a bog.)

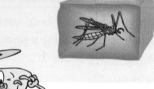

But No One Knows How Life Began

Fossils show how many of today's species have <u>evolved</u> (changed and developed) over millions of years. But where did the <u>first</u> living thing come from...

1) There are various <u>hypotheses</u> suggesting how life first came into being, but no one really <u>knows</u>.

2) Maybe the first life forms came into existence in a primordial <u>swamp</u> (or under the <u>sea</u>) here on <u>Earth</u>. Maybe simple organic molecules were brought to Earth on <u>comets</u> — these could have then become more <u>complex</u> organic molecules, and eventually very simple <u>life forms</u>.

3) These hypotheses can't be supported or disproved because there's a <u>lack</u> of <u>valid</u> and <u>reliable</u> evidence.

4) There's a lack of evidence because scientists believe many early organisms were <u>soft-bodied</u>, and soft tissue tends to decay away <u>completely</u>. So the fossil record is <u>incomplete</u>.

Validity and reliability are explained on page 2.

5) Plus, fossils that did form millions of years ago may have been <u>destroyed</u> by <u>geological activity</u>. e.g. the movement of tectonic plates may have crushed fossils already formed in the rock.

Don't get bogged down by all this information...

It's a bit mind-boggling really, how <u>fossils</u> of organisms can still exist even millions of years after they died. Right, testing time... scribble down the <u>three ways</u> that fossils form and why we can't be sure <u>how life began</u>.

Extinction and Speciation

Evolution leads to the development of lots of <u>different species</u>. But not every species is still around today... :(

Extinction Happens if You Can't Evolve Quickly Enough

The fossil record contains many species that <u>don't exist any more</u> — these species are said to be <u>extinct</u>.
<u>Dinosaurs</u> and <u>mammoths</u> are extinct animals, with only <u>fossils</u> to tell us they existed at all.

Species become extinct for these reasons:
1) The <u>environment changes</u> too quickly (e.g. destruction of habitat).
2) A <u>new predator</u> kills them all (e.g. humans hunting them).
3) A <u>new disease</u> kills them all.
4) They can't <u>compete</u> with another (new) species for <u>food</u>.
5) A <u>catastrophic event</u> happens that kills them all
   (e.g. a volcanic eruption or a collision with an asteroid).
6) A <u>new species</u> develops (this is called speciation — see below).

Dodos are now extinct. Humans not only hunted them, but introduced other animals which ate all their eggs, and we destroyed the forest where they lived — they really didn't stand a chance...

Speciation is the Development of a New Species

1) A species is a group of <u>similar organisms</u> that can <u>reproduce</u> to give <u>fertile offspring</u>.
2) <u>Speciation</u> is the development of a <u>new species</u>.
3) Speciation occurs when <u>populations</u> of the <u>same species</u> become so <u>different</u>
   that they can <u>no longer breed</u> together to produce <u>fertile offspring</u>.

Isolation and Natural Selection Lead to Speciation

<u>Isolation</u> is where <u>populations</u> of a species are <u>separated</u>. This can happen due to a <u>physical barrier</u>.
E.g. floods and earthquakes can cause barriers that <u>geographically isolate</u> some individuals from the main population. <u>Conditions</u> on either side of the barrier will be <u>slightly different</u>, e.g. they may have <u>different climates</u>. Because the environment is <u>different</u> on each side, <u>different characteristics</u> will become more common in each population due to <u>natural selection</u>:

1) Each population shows <u>variation</u> because they have a wide range of <u>alleles</u>.
2) In each population, individuals with characteristics that make them better adapted to their environment have a <u>better chance of survival</u> and so are more likely to <u>breed</u> successfully.
3) So the <u>alleles</u> that control the <u>beneficial characteristics</u> are more likely to be <u>passed on</u> to the <u>next generation</u>.

Eventually, individuals from the different populations will have <u>changed</u> so much that they <u>won't</u> be able to <u>breed</u> with one another to produce fertile offspring. The two groups will have become <u>separate species</u>.

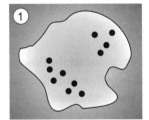 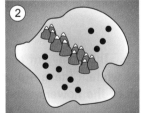 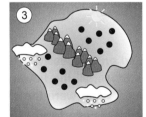 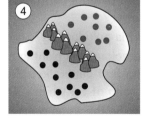

Two populations of the same species ⇒ Physical barriers separate populations. ⇒ Populations adapt to new environments. ⇒ Development of a new species.
• = individual organism

Up for grabs — a top quality gag about speciation...going once...going twice...

So <u>speciation</u> happens if two or more populations of the same species change so much that they can <u>no longer breed together</u> to produce <u>fertile offspring</u>. It's caused by the populations becoming <u>separated</u> from each other. Right, I think it must be nearly time for a break before your brain cells become extinct...

Revision Summary for Biology 2b

Wow, that was quite a long section. First there was all the stuff on enzymes and then came all the geneticsy bits. And just to finish off, some questions. Use these to find out what you know about it all — and what you don't. Then look back and learn the bits you don't know. Then try the questions again, and again...

1) Give a definition of a catalyst.
2) State three functions of proteins in living cells, other than acting as catalysts.
3) Explain why an enzyme-catalysed reaction stops when the reaction mixture is heated above a certain temperature.
4) In which three places in the body is amylase produced?
5) Where in the body is bile: a) produced? b) stored? c) used?
6) Explain why the stomach produces hydrochloric acid.
7) Write down the word equation for aerobic respiration.
8) Give two examples of how an animal uses the energy released by aerobic respiration.
9) What is anaerobic respiration? Give the word equation for anaerobic respiration in our bodies.
10) Explain how you repay an oxygen debt.
11) Give two kinds of enzyme that would be useful in a biological washing powder.
12) Discuss the advantages and disadvantages of using enzymes in industry.
13) Explain how DNA controls the activities of a cell.
14) Explain how DNA fingerprinting is used in forensic science.
15) What is mitosis used for in the human body? Describe the four steps in mitosis.
16) Name the other type of cell division, and say where it happens in the body of a human male.
17) What is differentiation in a cell?
18) Give three ways that embryonic stem cells could be used to cure diseases.
19) Which chromosome in the human body causes male characteristics?
20) Copy and complete the diagrams to show what happens to the X and Y chromosomes during reproduction.
21) List three important conclusions that Mendel reached following his experiments with pea plants.

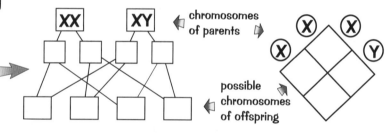

22) The significance of Mendel's work was not realised until 1900, 16 years after Mendel died. Suggest why the importance of the work wasn't understood at the time.
23) What is an allele?
24) What is meant by an organism being heterozygous? What about homozygous?
25) Describe the basic difference between a recessive allele and a dominant one.
26) If both parents carry recessive allele for cystic fibrosis, what is the probability of their child being a carrier?
27) What is polydactyly?
28)*Blue colour in a plant is carried on a recessive allele, b. The dominant allele, B, gives white flowers. In the first generation after a cross, all the flowers are white. These are bred together and the result is a ratio of 54 white : 19 blue. What were the alleles of the flowers used in the first cross?
29) Describe the three ways that fossils can form. Give an example of each type.
30) Give three reasons why some species become extinct.
31) What is speciation? Explain how geographical isolation can lead to speciation.

* Answers on page 108.

Atoms, Compounds and Isotopes

Remember atoms? They're the <u>small</u> but important guys. Just to refresh your memory, they contain <u>three</u> even smaller types of particle — <u>protons</u>, <u>neutrons</u> and <u>electrons</u>.

Atomic Number and Mass Number Describe an Atom

These two numbers tell you how many of each kind of particle an atom has.

The Mass Number
— Total number of
protons and neutrons

The Atomic Number
— Number of protons

$^{23}_{11}\text{Na}$

1) The <u>atomic number</u> tells you how many <u>protons</u> there are.

2) Atoms of the <u>same</u> element all have the <u>same</u> number of <u>protons</u> — so atoms of <u>different</u> elements will have <u>different</u> numbers of <u>protons</u>.

3) To get the number of <u>neutrons</u>, just <u>subtract</u> the <u>atomic number</u> from the <u>mass number</u>. Electrons aren't counted in the mass number because their <u>relative mass</u> is very small.

PARTICLE	MASS
Proton	1
Neutron	1
Electron	very small

Compounds Are Chemically Bonded

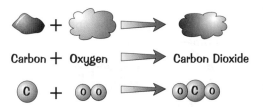

Carbon + Oxygen ⟹ Carbon Dioxide

C + O O ⟹ O C O

1) Compounds are formed when <u>atoms</u> of <u>two or more</u> elements are <u>chemically combined</u> together. For example, carbon dioxide is a <u>compound</u> formed from a <u>chemical reaction</u> between carbon and oxygen.

2) It's difficult to <u>separate</u> the two original elements out again.

Isotopes Are the Same Except for an Extra Neutron or Two

A favourite exam question: "<u>Explain what is meant by the term isotope</u>". <u>LEARN</u> the definition:

> Isotopes are: <u>different atomic forms</u> of the <u>same element</u>, which have the <u>SAME</u> number of <u>PROTONS</u> but a <u>DIFFERENT</u> number of <u>NEUTRONS</u>.

1) The upshot is: isotopes must have the <u>same</u> atomic number but <u>different</u> mass numbers.

2) <u>If</u> they had <u>different</u> atomic numbers, they'd be <u>different</u> elements altogether.

3) <u>Carbon-12</u> and <u>carbon-14</u> are a very popular pair of isotopes.

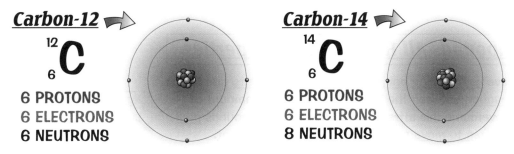

Carbon-12 ⟹
$^{12}_{6}\text{C}$
6 PROTONS
6 ELECTRONS
6 NEUTRONS

Carbon-14 ⟹
$^{14}_{6}\text{C}$
6 PROTONS
6 ELECTRONS
8 NEUTRONS

Will this be in your exam — isotope so...

... because obviously you'll know it as well as you know not to eat yellow snow. Anyway... it's really important you understand that an isotope is just a slight variation on the <u>same element</u>. Not so crazy really.

Ionic Bonding

Ionic Bonding — Transferring Electrons

In ionic bonding, atoms lose or gain electrons to form charged particles (called ions) which are then strongly attracted to one another (because of the attraction of opposite charges, + and –).

A Shell with Just One Electron is Well Keen to Get Rid...

All the atoms over at the left-hand side of the periodic table, e.g. sodium, potassium, calcium etc. have just one or two electrons in their outer shell (highest energy level). And they're pretty keen to get shot of them, because then they'll only have full shells left, which is how they like it. (They try to have the same electronic structure as a noble gas.) So given half a chance they do get rid, and that leaves the atom as an ion instead. Now ions aren't the kind of things that sit around quietly watching the world go by. They tend to leap at the first passing ion with an opposite charge and stick to it like glue.

A Nearly Full Shell is Well Keen to Get That Extra Electron...

On the other side of the periodic table, the elements in Group 6 and Group 7, such as oxygen and chlorine, have outer shells which are nearly full. They're obviously pretty keen to gain that extra one or two electrons to fill the shell up. When they do of course they become ions (you know, not the kind of things to sit around) and before you know it, pop, they've latched onto the atom (ion) that gave up the electron a moment earlier. The reaction of sodium and chlorine is a classic case:

The sodium atom gives up its outer electron and becomes an Na$^+$ ion.

The chlorine atom has picked up the spare electron and becomes a Cl$^-$ ion.

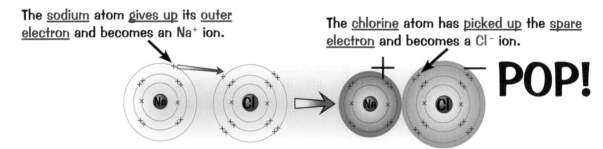

POP!

Ionic Compounds Have A Regular Lattice Structure

1) Ionic compounds always have giant ionic lattices.
2) The ions form a closely packed regular lattice arrangement.
3) There are very strong electrostatic forces of attraction between oppositely charged ions, in all directions.
4) A single crystal of sodium chloride (salt) is one giant ionic lattice, which is why salt crystals tend to be cuboid in shape. The Na$^+$ and Cl$^-$ ions are held together in a regular lattice.

● = Cl$^-$
● = Na$^+$

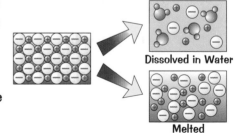

Ionic Compounds All Have Similar Properties

1) They all have high melting points and high boiling points due to the strong attraction between the ions. It takes a large amount of energy to overcome this attraction. When ionic compounds melt, the ions are free to move and they'll carry electric current.
2) They do dissolve easily in water though. The ions separate and are all free to move in the solution, so they'll carry electric current.

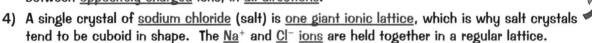

Dissolved in Water

Melted

Giant ionic lattices — all over your chips...

These guys are tough nuts to crack, but if you do crack 'em, they get all excited and start conducting electricity.

Ions and Formulas

Make sure you've really got your head around the idea of ionic bonding before you start on this page.

Groups 1& 2 and 6 & 7 are the Most Likely to Form Ions

1) Remember, atoms that have <u>lost</u> or <u>gained</u> an electron (or electrons) are <u>ions</u>.

2) Ions have the <u>electronic structure</u> of a <u>noble gas</u>.

3) The elements that most readily form ions are those in <u>Groups 1</u>, <u>2</u>, <u>6 and 7</u>.

4) <u>Group 1 and 2 elements</u> are <u>metals</u> and they <u>lose</u> electrons to form <u>positive ions</u>.

5) For example, <u>Group 1</u> elements (the <u>alkali metals</u>) form ionic compounds with <u>non-metals</u> where the metal ion has a 1^+ charge. E.g. K^+Cl^-.

6) <u>Group 6 and 7 elements</u> are <u>non-metals</u>. They <u>gain</u> electrons to form <u>negative ions</u>.

7) For example, <u>Group 7</u> elements (the <u>halogens</u>) form ionic compounds with the <u>alkali metals</u> where the halide ion has a 1^- charge. E.g. Na^+Cl^-.

8) The <u>charge</u> on the <u>positive ions</u> is the <u>same</u> as the <u>group number</u> of the element:

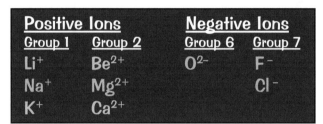

Positive Ions		Negative Ions	
Group 1	Group 2	Group 6	Group 7
Li^+	Be^{2+}	O^{2-}	F^-
Na^+	Mg^{2+}		Cl^-
K^+	Ca^{2+}		

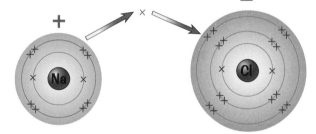

9) Any of the positive ions above can <u>combine</u> with any of the negative ions to form an <u>ionic compound</u>.

10) Only elements at <u>opposite sides</u> of the periodic table will form ionic compounds, e.g. Na and Cl, where one of them becomes a <u>positive ion</u> and one becomes a <u>negative ion</u>.

> Remember, the + and – charges we talk about, e.g. Na^+ for sodium, just tell you <u>what type of ion the atom WILL FORM</u> in a chemical reaction. In sodium <u>metal</u> there are <u>only neutral sodium atoms, Na</u>. The Na^+ ions <u>will only appear</u> if the sodium metal <u>reacts</u> with something like water or chlorine.

Look at Charges to Work Out the Formula of an Ionic Compound

1) Ionic compounds are made up of a <u>positively charged</u> part and a <u>negatively charged</u> part.

2) The <u>overall charge</u> of <u>any compound</u> is <u>zero</u>.

3) So all the <u>negative charges</u> in the compound must <u>balance</u> all the <u>positive charges</u>.

4) You can use the charges on the <u>individual ions</u> present to work out the formula for the ionic compound:

> Sodium chloride contains Na^+ (+1) and Cl^- (–1) ions.
>
> (+1) + (–1) = 0. The charges are balanced with one of each ion, so the formula for sodium chloride = NaCl

> Magnesium chloride contains Mg^{2+} (+2) and Cl^- (–1) ions.
>
> Because a chloride ion only has a 1^- charge we will need <u>two</u> of them to balance out the 2^+ charge of a magnesium ion. This gives us the formula $MgCl_2$.

The formula for exam success = revision...

Remember, the + and – charges only appear when an element <u>reacts</u> with something. So, don't be fooling yourself, sodium isn't always a flashy Na^+ ion — when he's being sodium metal he's just made up of boring old <u>neutral sodium atoms, Na</u>. But wave some chlorine at him and he gets positively charged.

Electronic Structure of Ions

I heard the examiner fancies himself as a bit of an artist. This page is full of lovely drawings of <u>electronic structures</u> that should put a smile on his face.

Show the Electronic Structure of Simple Ions With Diagrams

A useful way of representing ions is by <u>drawing</u> out their electronic structure. Just use a big <u>square bracket</u> and a + or − to show the charge. A few <u>ions</u> and the <u>ionic compounds</u> they form are shown below. You need to know how to draw them:

Sodium Chloride

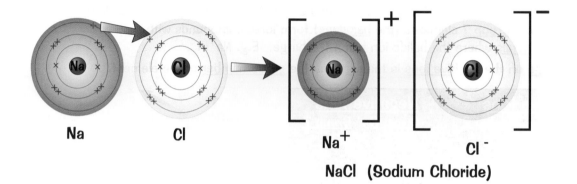

Na   Cl   Na$^+$ Cl$^-$

NaCl (Sodium Chloride)

Magnesium Oxide

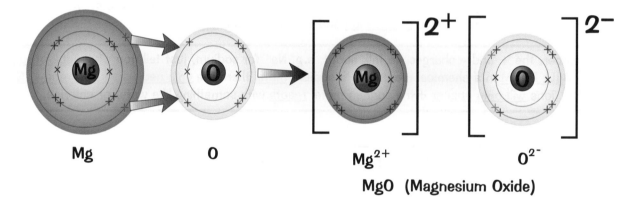

Mg   O   Mg^{2+} O^{2-}

MgO (Magnesium Oxide)

Calcium Chloride

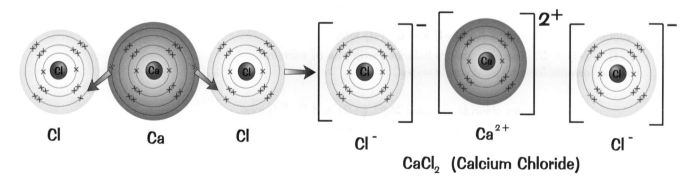

Cl   Ca   Cl   Cl$^-$ Ca^{2+} Cl$^-$

CaCl$_2$ (Calcium Chloride)

Any old ion, any old ion — any, any, any old ion...

3 ionic compounds, 3 drawings, 1 exam hall. It's like the start of a bad Game Show. Whether or not you're able to produce some lovely drawings of these bad boys all comes down to how well you've understood <u>ionic bonding</u>. (So if you're struggling, try reading the last few pages again — I know I had to).

Covalent Bonding

Some elements bond ionically (see page 40) but others form strong <u>covalent bonds</u>.
This is where atoms <u>share electrons</u> with each other so that they've got <u>full outer shells</u>.

Covalent Bonds — Sharing Electrons

1) Sometimes atoms prefer to make <u>covalent bonds</u> by <u>sharing</u> electrons with other atoms.

2) They only share electrons in their <u>outer shells</u> (highest energy levels).

3) This way <u>both</u> atoms feel that they have a <u>full outer shell</u>, and that makes them happy. Having a full outer shell gives them the electronic structure of a <u>noble gas</u>.

4) Each <u>covalent bond</u> provides one <u>extra</u> shared electron for each atom.

5) So, a covalent bond is a <u>shared pair</u> of electrons.

6) Each atom involved has to make <u>enough</u> covalent bonds to <u>fill up</u> its outer shell.

7) <u>Learn</u> these <u>seven important examples</u>:

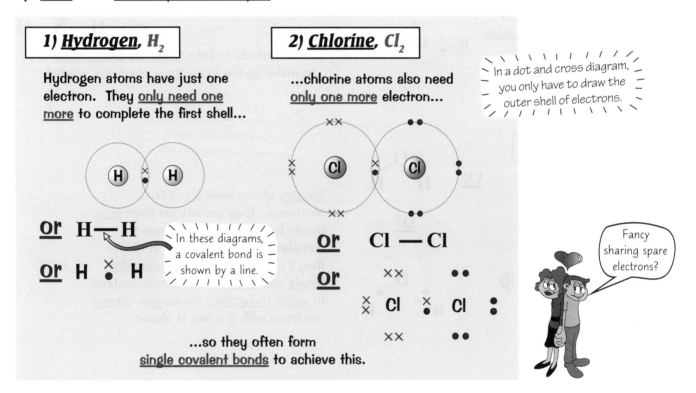

1) Hydrogen, H_2

Hydrogen atoms have just one electron. They <u>only need one more</u> to complete the first shell...

or H—H

or H $\overset{\times}{\bullet}$ H

In these diagrams, a covalent bond is shown by a line.

2) Chlorine, Cl_2

...chlorine atoms also need <u>only one more</u> electron...

or Cl — Cl

...so they often form <u>single covalent bonds</u> to achieve this.

In a dot and cross diagram, you only have to draw the outer shell of electrons.

Fancy sharing spare electrons?

3) Methane, CH_4

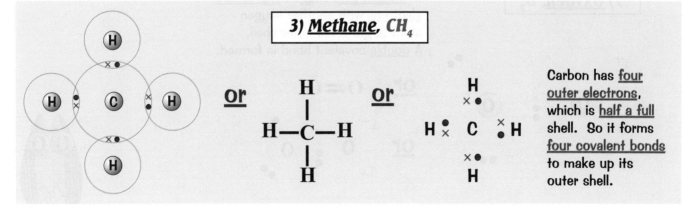

or H—C—H (with H above and below C)

Carbon has <u>four outer electrons</u>, which is <u>half a full</u> shell. So it forms <u>four covalent bonds</u> to make up its outer shell.

Covalent bonding — it's good to share...

There's another page of covalent bonding diagrams yet to come, but make sure you can draw the diagrams for the covalent compounds on this page first. When you've drawn a dot and cross diagram, it's a really good idea to count up the number of electrons, just to <u>double check</u> you've definitely got a full outer shell.

More Covalent Bonding

You lucky thing. There are four more examples of covalent bonding on this page — and for each compound there are three possible <u>diagrams</u>. I make that twelve diagrams in total... and just a smattering of words. So, this page is a breeze compared to others out there.

4) Hydrogen Chloride, HCl

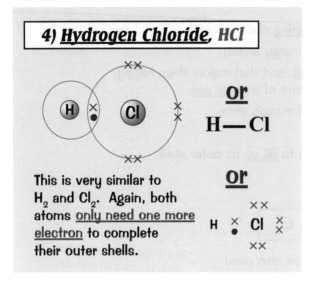

or H—Cl

or

This is very similar to H_2 and Cl_2. Again, both atoms <u>only need one more electron</u> to complete their outer shells.

5) Ammonia, NH₃

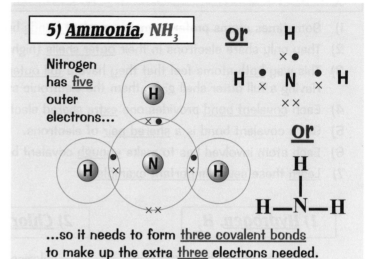

Nitrogen has <u>five</u> outer electrons...

...so it needs to form <u>three covalent bonds</u> to make up the extra <u>three</u> electrons needed.

Remember — it's only the outer shells that share electrons with each other.

6) Water, H₂O

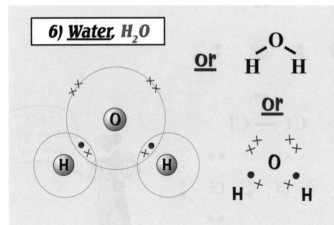

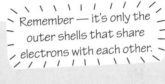

<u>Oxygen</u> atoms have <u>six</u> outer electrons. They sometimes form <u>ionic</u> bonds by <u>taking</u> two electrons to complete their outer shell. However they'll also cheerfully form <u>covalent bonds</u> and <u>share</u> two electrons instead. In <u>water molecules</u>, the oxygen <u>shares</u> electrons with the two H atoms.

7) Oxygen, O₂

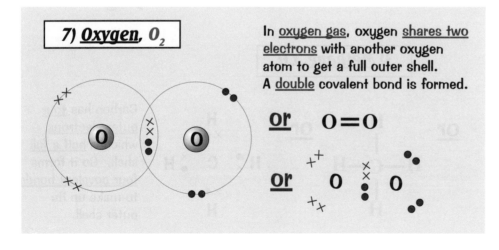

In <u>oxygen gas</u>, oxygen <u>shares two electrons</u> with another oxygen atom to get a full outer shell. A <u>double</u> covalent bond is formed.

or O=O

The name's Bond, Covalent Bond...

Make sure you learn these seven really basic examples and <u>why they work</u>. Every atom wants a full outer shell, and they can get that either by becoming an <u>ion</u> (see page 40) or by <u>sharing electrons</u>. Once you understand that, you should be able to apply it to any example they give you in the exam.

Covalent Substances: Two Kinds

Substances with <u>covalent bonds</u> (electron sharing) can either be <u>simple molecules</u> or <u>giant structures</u>.

Simple Molecular Substances

1) The atoms form <u>very strong</u> covalent bonds to form <u>small</u> molecules of several atoms.
2) By contrast, the forces of attraction <u>between</u> these molecules are <u>very weak</u>.
3) The result of these feeble <u>intermolecular forces</u> is that the <u>melting</u> and <u>boiling points</u> are <u>very low</u>, because the molecules are <u>easily parted</u> from each other. It's the <u>intermolecular forces</u> that get <u>broken</u> when simple molecular substances melt or boil — <u>not</u> the much <u>stronger covalent bonds</u>.
4) Most molecular substances are <u>gases or liquids</u> at room temperature, but they can be <u>solids</u>.
5) Molecular substances <u>don't conduct electricity</u> — there are <u>no ions</u> so there's <u>no electrical charge</u>.

Very weak intermolecular forces

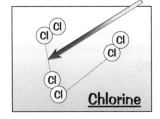 Chlorine
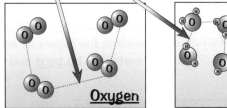 Oxygen
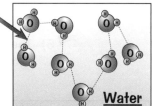 Water

Giant Covalent Structures Are Macromolecules

1) These are similar to giant ionic structures (lattices) <u>except</u> that there are <u>no charged ions</u>.
2) <u>All</u> the atoms are <u>bonded</u> to <u>each other</u> by <u>strong</u> covalent bonds.
3) This means that they have <u>very high</u> melting and boiling points.
4) They <u>don't conduct electricity</u> — not even when <u>molten</u> (except for graphite).
5) The <u>main examples</u> are <u>diamond</u> and <u>graphite</u>, which are both made only from <u>carbon atoms</u>, and <u>silicon dioxide</u> (silica).

Diamond

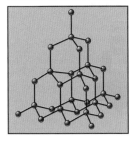

Each carbon atom forms <u>four covalent bonds</u> in a <u>very rigid</u> giant covalent structure.
This structure makes diamond the <u>hardest</u> natural substance, so it's used for drill tips.
And it's <u>pretty</u> and <u>sparkly</u> too.

Silicon Dioxide (Silica)

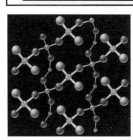

Sometimes called <u>silica</u>, this is what <u>sand</u> is made of.
Each grain of sand is <u>one giant structure</u> of silicon and oxygen.

Graphite

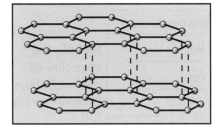

Each carbon atom only forms <u>three covalent bonds</u>. This creates <u>layers</u> which are free to <u>slide over each other</u>, like a pack of cards — so graphite is <u>soft</u> and <u>slippery</u>. The layers are held together so loosely that they can be <u>rubbed off</u> onto paper — that's how a <u>pencil</u> works. This is because there are <u>weak intermolecular forces</u> between the layers.

Graphite is the only <u>non-metal</u> which is a <u>good conductor of heat and electricity</u>. Each carbon atom has one <u>delocalised</u> (free) electron and it's these free electrons that <u>conduct</u> heat and electricity.

Carbon is a girl's best friend...

The <u>two different types</u> of covalent substance are very different — make sure you know about them both.
You should be able to recognise a <u>giant structure</u> by looking at diagrams of its <u>bonding</u>.

Metallic Structures

Ever wondered what makes <u>metals</u> tick? Well, either way, this is the page for you.

Metal Properties <u>*Are All Due to the*</u> Sea of Free Electrons

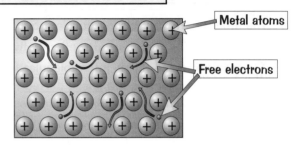
Metal atoms

Free electrons

1) <u>Metals</u> also consist of a <u>giant structure</u>.

2) <u>Metallic bonds</u> involve the all-important '<u>free electrons</u>' which produce <u>all</u> the properties of metals. These delocalised (free) electrons come from the <u>outer shell</u> of <u>every</u> metal atom in the structure.

3) These electrons are <u>free to move</u> through the whole structure and so metals are good conductors of <u>heat and electricity</u>.

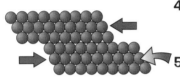

4) These electrons also <u>hold</u> the <u>atoms</u> together in a <u>regular</u> structure. There are strong forces of <u>electrostatic attraction</u> between the <u>positive metal ions</u> and the <u>negative electrons</u>.

5) They also allow the layers of atoms to <u>slide</u> over each other, allowing metals to be <u>bent</u> and <u>shaped</u>.

Alloys <u>are Harder</u> <u>Than</u> Pure Metals

1) <u>Pure metals</u> often aren't quite right for certain jobs. So scientists <u>mix two or more metals together</u> — creating an <u>alloy</u> with the properties they want.

2) Different elements have <u>different sized atoms</u>. So when another metal is mixed with a pure metal, the new metal atoms will <u>distort</u> the layers of metal atoms, making it more difficult for them to slide over each other. So alloys are <u>harder</u>.

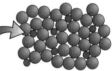

Identifying <u>the Structure of a Substance</u> <u>by Its Properties</u>

You should be able to easily <u>identify</u> most substances just by the way they <u>behave</u> as either:

That's the guy.

- <u>giant ionic</u>,
- <u>simple molecular</u>,
- <u>giant covalent</u>,
- or <u>giant metallic</u>.

The way they might test you in the Exam is by describing the <u>physical properties</u> of a substance and asking you to decide <u>which type of structure</u> it has. Try this one:

<u>Example</u>: Four substances were tested for various properties with the following results:

Substance	Melting point (°C)	Boiling point (°C)	Good electrical conductor?
A	−218.4	−182.96	No
B	1535	2750	Yes
C	1410	2355	No
D	801	1413	When molten

Identify the structure of each substance. (Answers on page 108.)

A few free electrons and my knees have gone all bendy...

You have to be able to identify the structure of <u>any</u> substance based on its properties — and explain <u>why</u>.

New Materials

New materials are continually being developed, with new properties. The two groups of materials you really need to know about are <u>smart materials</u> and <u>nanoparticles</u>.

Smart Materials Have Some Really Weird Properties

1) <u>Smart</u> materials <u>behave differently</u> depending on the <u>conditions</u>, e.g. temperature.

2) A good example is <u>nitinol</u> — a "<u>shape memory alloy</u>". It's a metal <u>alloy</u> (about half nickel, half titanium) but when it's cool you can <u>bend it</u> and <u>twist it</u> like rubber. Bend it too far, though, and it stays bent. But here's the really clever bit — if you heat it above a certain temperature, it goes back to a "<u>remembered</u>" shape.

3) It's really handy for <u>glasses frames</u>. If you accidentally bend them, you can just pop them into a bowl of hot water and they'll <u>jump</u> back <u>into shape</u>.

4) Nitinol is also used for <u>dental braces</u>. In the mouth it <u>warms</u> and tries to return to a 'remembered' shape, and so it gently <u>pulls the teeth</u> with it.

Nanoparticles Are Really Really Really Really Tiny   ...smaller than that.

1) Really tiny particles, <u>1–100 nanometres</u> across, are called 'nanoparticles' (1 nm = 0.000 000 001 m).

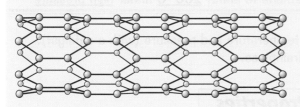

2) Nanoparticles contain roughly <u>a few hundred atoms</u>.

3) Nanoparticles include <u>fullerenes</u>. These are molecules of <u>carbon</u>, shaped like <u>hollow balls</u> or <u>closed tubes</u>. The carbon atoms are arranged in <u>hexagonal rings</u>. Different fullerenes contain <u>different numbers</u> of carbon atoms.

4) A nanoparticle has very <u>different properties</u> from the 'bulk' chemical that it's made from — e.g. <u>fullerenes</u> have different properties from big <u>lumps of carbon</u>.

1) Fullerenes can be joined together to form <u>nanotubes</u> — teeny tiny hollow carbon tubes, a few nanometres across.

2) All those covalent bonds make carbon nanotubes <u>very strong</u>. They can be used to reinforce graphite in <u>tennis rackets</u>.

5) Using nanoparticles is known as <u>nanoscience</u>. Many <u>new uses</u> of nanoparticles are being developed:

- They have a <u>huge surface area to volume ratio</u>, so they could help make new industrial <u>catalysts</u> (see page 60).

- You can use nanoparticles to make <u>sensors</u> to detect one type of molecule and nothing else. These <u>highly specific</u> sensors are already being used to test water purity.

- Nanotubes can be used to make <u>stronger</u>, <u>lighter</u> building materials.

- New cosmetics, e.g. <u>sun tan cream</u> and <u>deodorant</u>, have been made using nanoparticles. The small particles do their job but don't leave <u>white marks</u> on the skin.

- <u>Nanomedicine</u> is a hot topic. The idea is that tiny fullerenes are <u>absorbed</u> more easily by the body than most particles. This means they could <u>deliver drugs</u> right into the cells where they're needed.

- New <u>lubricant coatings</u> are being developed using fullerenes. These coatings reduce friction a bit like <u>ball bearings</u> and could be used in all sorts of places from <u>artificial joints</u> to <u>gears</u>.

- Nanotubes <u>conduct</u> electricity, so they can be used in tiny <u>electric circuits</u> for computer chips.

Bendy specs, tennis rackets and computer chips — cool...

Some nanoparticles have really <u>unexpected properties</u>. Silver's normally very unreactive, but silver nanoparticles can kill bacteria. Cool. On the flipside, we also need to watch out for any unexpected harmful properties.

Polymers

There's plastic and there's... well, plastic. You wouldn't want to make a chair with the same plastic that gets used for flimsy old carrier bags. But whatever the plastic, it's always a polymer.

Forces Between Molecules Determine the Properties of Plastics

Strong covalent bonds hold the atoms together in long chains. But it's the bonds between the different molecule chains that determine the properties of the plastic.

Weak Forces:
Individual tangled chains of polymers, held together by weak intermolecular forces, are free to slide over each other.

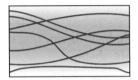

Strong Forces:
Some plastics have stronger intermolecular forces between the polymer chains, called crosslinks, that hold the chains firmly together.

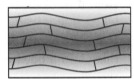

THERMOSOFTENING POLYMERS don't have cross-linking between chains. The forces between the chains are really easy to overcome, so it's dead easy to melt the plastic. When it cools, the polymer hardens into a new shape. You can melt these plastics and remould them as many times as you like.

THERMOSETTING POLYMERS have crosslinks. These hold the chains together in a solid structure. The polymer doesn't soften when it's heated. Thermosetting polymers are the tough guys of the plastic world. They're strong, hard and rigid.

How You Make a Polymer Affects Its Properties

1) The starting materials and reaction conditions will both affect the properties of a polymer.

2) Two types of polythene can be made using different conditions:

- Low density (LD) polythene is made by heating ethene to about 200 °C under high pressure. It's flexible and is used for bags and bottles.

- High density (HD) polythene is made at a lower temperature and pressure (with a catalyst). It's more rigid and is used for water tanks and drainpipes.

The Use of a Plastic Depends on Its Properties

You might need to answer a question like this one in the exam.

Choose from the table the plastic that would be best suited for making:

a) a disposable cup for hot drinks,

b) clothing,

c) a measuring cylinder.

Give reasons for each choice.

Plastic	Cost	Resistance to chemicals	Melting point	Transparency	Rigidity	Can be made into fibres
W	High	High	High	Low	High	No
X	Low	Low	Low	Low	Low	Yes
Y	High	High	High	High	High	No
Z	Low	Low	High	High	High	No

Answers

a) Z — low cost (disposable) and high melting point (for hot drinks),

b) X — flexible (essential for clothing) and able to be made into fibres (clothing is usually woven),

c) Y — transparent and resistant to chemicals (you need to be able to see the liquid inside and the liquid and measuring cylinder mustn't react with each other).

Platinum cards — my favourite sort of plastic...

You need to learn the properties of thermosoftening and thermosetting polymers. But you also might be given information about the properties of a certain polymer and have to explain why it's suited to its use.

Relative Formula Mass

The biggest trouble with <u>relative atomic mass</u> and <u>relative formula mass</u> is that they <u>sound</u> so blood-curdling. Take a few deep breaths, and just enjoy, as the mists slowly clear...

Relative Atomic Mass, A_r — Easy Peasy

1) This is just a way of saying how <u>heavy</u> different atoms are <u>compared</u> with the mass of an atom of carbon-12. So carbon-12 has A_r of <u>exactly 12</u>.

2) It turns out that the <u>relative atomic mass</u> A_r is usually just the same as the <u>mass number</u> of the element.

3) In the periodic table, the elements all have <u>two</u> numbers. The smaller one is the atomic number (how many protons it has). But the <u>bigger one</u> is the <u>mass number</u> or <u>relative atomic mass</u>.

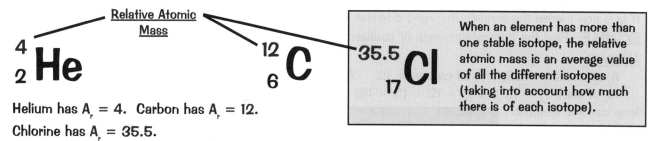

Helium has A_r = 4. Carbon has A_r = 12.
Chlorine has A_r = 35.5.

When an element has more than one stable isotope, the relative atomic mass is an average value of all the different isotopes (taking into account how much there is of each isotope).

Relative Formula Mass, M_r — Also Easy Peasy

If you have a compound like $MgCl_2$ then it has a <u>relative formula mass</u>, M_r, which is just all the relative atomic masses <u>added together</u>.
For $MgCl_2$ it would be:

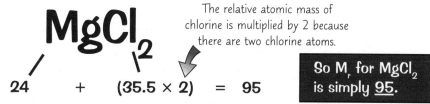

The relative atomic mass of chlorine is multiplied by 2 because there are two chlorine atoms.

So M_r for $MgCl_2$ is simply <u>95</u>.

You can easily get A_r for any element from the periodic table (see inside front cover), but in a lot of questions they give you them anyway. And that's all it is. A big fancy name like <u>relative formula mass</u> and all it means is "<u>add up all the relative atomic masses</u>". What a swizz, eh?

"ONE MOLE" of a Substance is Equal to its M_r in Grams

The <u>relative formula mass</u> (A_r or M_r) of a substance <u>in grams</u> is known as <u>one mole</u> of that substance.

<u>Examples:</u>
Iron has an A_r of 56.
Nitrogen gas, N_2, has an M_r of 28 (2×14).

So one mole of iron weighs exactly 56 g
So one mole of N_2 weighs exactly 28 g

You can convert between moles and grams using this formula:

$$\text{NUMBER OF MOLES} = \frac{\text{Mass in g (of element or compound)}}{M_r \text{ (of element or compound)}}$$

<u>Example:</u> How many moles are there in 42 g of carbon?
<u>Answer:</u> No. of moles = Mass (g) / M_r = 42/12 = <u>3.5 moles</u>   Easy Peasy

Numbers? — and you thought you were doing chemistry...

Learn the definitions of <u>relative atomic mass</u> and <u>relative formula mass</u>, then have a go at these:
1) Use the periodic table to find the relative atomic mass of these elements: Cu, K, Kr, Cl
2) Find the relative formula mass of: NaOH, Fe_2O_3, C_6H_{14}, $Mg(NO_3)_2$ Answers on page 108.

Two Formula Mass Calculations

Although relative atomic mass and relative formula mass are <u>easy enough</u>, it can get just a tad <u>trickier</u> when you start getting into other calculations which use them. It depends on how good your maths is basically, because it's all to do with ratios and percentages.

Calculating % Mass of an Element in a Compound

This is actually dead easy — so long as you've learnt this formula:

$$\text{Percentage mass OF AN ELEMENT IN A COMPOUND} = \frac{A_r \times \text{No. of atoms (of that element)}}{M_r \text{ (of whole compound)}} \times 100$$

If you don't learn the formula then you'd better be pretty smart — or you'll struggle.

<u>EXAMPLE:</u> Find the percentage mass of sodium in sodium carbonate, Na_2CO_3.

<u>ANSWER:</u>

A_r of sodium = 23, A_r of carbon = 12, A_r of oxygen = 16

M_r of Na_2CO_3 = $(2 \times 23) + 12 + (3 \times 16) = 106$

Now use the formula:

$$\underline{\text{Percentage mass}} = \frac{A_r \times n}{M_r} \times 100 = \frac{23 \times 2}{106} \times 100 = 43.4\%$$

And there you have it. Sodium makes up <u>43.4%</u> of the mass of sodium carbonate.

Finding the Empirical Formula (from Masses or Percentages)

This also sounds a lot worse than it really is. Try this for an easy peasy <u>stepwise method</u>:

1) <u>List all the elements</u> in the compound (there's usually only two or three!)
2) <u>Underneath them</u>, write their <u>experimental masses or percentages</u>.
3) <u>Divide</u> each mass or percentage <u>by the A_r</u> for that particular element.
4) Turn the numbers you get into <u>a nice simple ratio</u> by multiplying and/or dividing them by well-chosen numbers.
5) Get the ratio in its <u>simplest form</u>, and that tells you the <u>empirical formula</u> of the compound.

<u>Example:</u> Find the empirical formula of the iron oxide produced when 44.8 g of iron react with 19.2 g of oxygen. (A_r for iron = 56, A_r for oxygen = 16)

<u>Method:</u>

1) <u>List the two elements:</u>   Fe   O

2) Write in the <u>experimental masses</u>:   44.8   19.2

3) <u>Divide by the A_r</u> for each element: $\frac{44.8}{56} = 0.8$ $\frac{19.2}{16} = 1.2$

4) Multiply by 10...   8   12

     ...then divide by 4:   2   3

5) So the <u>simplest formula</u> is 2 atoms of Fe to 3 atoms of O, i.e. $\underline{Fe_2O_3}$. And that's it done.

> You need to realise (for the exam) that this <u>empirical method</u> (i.e. based on <u>experiment</u>) is the <u>only way</u> of finding out the formula of a compound. Rust is iron oxide, sure, but is it FeO, or Fe_2O_3? Only an experiment to determine the empirical formula will tell you for certain.

With this empirical formula I can rule the world! — mwa ha ha...

Make sure you learn the formula and the five steps in the red box. Then try these: Answers on page 108.

1) Find the percentage mass of oxygen in each of these: a) Fe_2O_3 b) H_2O c) $CaCO_3$ d) H_2SO_4.
2) Find the empirical formula of the compound formed from 2.4 g of carbon and 0.8 g of hydrogen.

Calculating Masses in Reactions

These can be kinda scary too, but chill out, little trembling one — just relax and enjoy.

The Three Important Steps — Not to Be Missed...

(Miss one out and it'll all go horribly wrong, believe me.)

> 1) <u>Write out</u> the balanced <u>equation</u>
> 2) <u>Work out M</u>$_r$ — just for the <u>two bits you want</u>
> 3) Apply the rule: <u>Divide to get one, then multiply to get all</u>
>   (But you have to apply this first to the substance they
>   give you information about, and then the other one!)

Don't worry — these steps should all make sense when you look at the example below.

<u>Example</u>: What mass of magnesium oxide is produced when 60 g of magnesium is burned in air?

<u>Answer</u>:

1) Write out the <u>balanced equation</u>: $2Mg + O_2 \rightarrow 2MgO$

2) Work out the <u>relative formula masses</u>:
   (don't do the oxygen — we don't need it)

$$2 \times 24 \rightarrow 2 \times (24+16)$$
$$48 \rightarrow 80$$

3) Apply the rule: <u>Divide to get one, then multiply to get all</u>:
   The two numbers, 48 and 80, tell us that <u>48 g of Mg react to give 80 g of MgO</u>.
   Here's the tricky bit. You've now got to be able to write this down:

> 48 g of Mg ......reacts to give.....80 g of MgO
>
> 1 g of Mg ......reacts to give.....
>
> 60 g of Mg .....reacts to give......

<u>The big clue</u> is that in the question they've said we want to burn "<u>60 g of magnesium</u>",
i.e. they've told us how much <u>magnesium</u> to have, and that's how you know to write down the
<u>left-hand side</u> of it first, because:

> We'll first need to ÷ by 48 to get 1 g of Mg
> and then need to × by 60 to get 60 g of Mg.

<u>Then</u> you can work out the numbers on the other side (shown in purple below) by realising that you must
<u>divide both sides by 48</u> and then <u>multiply both sides by 60</u>. It's tricky.

÷48 48 g of Mg .... 80 g of MgO ÷48
       1 g of Mg .... 1.67 g of MgO
×60 60 g of Mg .... 100 g of MgO ×60

The mass of product is called the <u>yield</u> of a reaction. You should realise that <u>in practice</u> you never get 100% of the yield, so the amount of product will be <u>slightly less than calculated</u> (see p.52).

This finally tells us that <u>60 g of magnesium will produce 100 g of magnesium oxide</u>.
If the question had said "Find how much magnesium gives 500 g of magnesium oxide", you'd fill in the
MgO side first, <u>because that's the one you'd have the information about</u>. Got it? Good-O!

Reaction mass calculations — no worries, matey...

The only way to get good at these is to practise. So have a go at these: Answers on page 108.
1) Find the mass of calcium which gives 30 g of calcium oxide (CaO) when burnt in air.
2) What mass of fluorine fully reacts with potassium to make 116 g of potassium fluoride (KF)?

Percentage Yield and Reversible Reactions

Percentage yield tells you about the <u>overall success</u> of an experiment. It compares what you calculate you should get (<u>predicted yield</u>) with what you get in practice (<u>actual yield</u>).

Percentage **Yield Compares Actual and Predicted Yield**

The amount of product you get is known as the <u>yield</u>. The more reactants you start with, the higher the <u>actual yield</u> will be — that's pretty obvious. But the <u>percentage yield doesn't</u> depend on the amount of reactants you started with — it's a <u>percentage</u>.

1) The <u>predicted yield</u> of a reaction can be calculated from the <u>balanced reaction equation</u>.

2) Percentage yield is given by the formula:

$$\text{percentage yield} = \frac{\text{actual yield (grams)}}{\text{predicted yield (grams)}} \times 100$$

(The predicted yield is sometimes called the theoretical yield.)

3) Percentage yield is <u>always</u> somewhere between 0 and 100%.

4) A 100% percentage yield means that you got <u>all</u> the product you expected to get.

5) A 0% yield means that <u>no</u> reactants were converted into product, i.e. no product at all was <u>made</u>.

Yields Are Always Less Than 100%

Even though <u>no atoms are gained or lost</u> in reactions, in real life, you <u>never</u> get a 100% percentage yield. Some product or reactant <u>always</u> gets lost along the way — and that goes for big <u>industrial processes</u> as well as school lab experiments. There are several reasons for this:

1) The reaction is <u>reversible</u>:

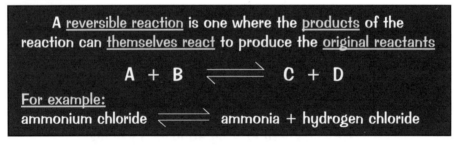

A <u>reversible reaction</u> is one where the <u>products</u> of the reaction can <u>themselves react</u> to produce the <u>original reactants</u>

A + B ⇌ C + D

<u>For example:</u>
ammonium chloride ⇌ ammonia + hydrogen chloride

This means that the reactants will never be completely converted to products because the reaction goes both ways. Some of the <u>products</u> are always <u>reacting together</u> to change back to the original reactants. This will mean a <u>lower yield</u>.

2) When you <u>filter a liquid</u> to remove <u>solid particles</u>, you nearly always <u>lose</u> a bit of liquid or a bit of solid. So, some of the product may be lost when it's <u>separated</u> from the reaction mixture.

3) Things don't always go exactly to plan. Sometimes there can be other <u>unexpected reactions</u> happening which <u>use up the reactants</u>. This means there's not as much reactant to make the <u>product</u> you want.

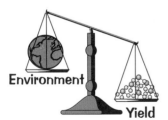

Environment
Yield

Thinking about product yield is important for <u>sustainable development</u>. Sustainable development is about making sure that we don't use <u>resources</u> faster than they can be <u>replaced</u> — there needs to be enough for <u>future generations</u> too. So, for example, using as <u>little energy</u> as possible to create the <u>highest product yield possible</u> means that resources are <u>saved</u>. A low yield means wasted chemicals — not very sustainable.

You can't always get what you want...

A high percentage yield means there's <u>not much waste</u> — which is good for <u>preserving resources</u>, and keeping production <u>costs down</u>. If a reaction's going to be worth doing commercially, it generally has to have a high percentage yield or recyclable reactants. Learn the <u>formula</u> for working out all important percentage yield.

Chemical Analysis and Instrumental Methods

Nowadays there are some pretty clever ways of <u>identifying</u> substances, from using filter paper to machines...

Artificial Colours Can Be Separated Using Paper Chromatography

A <u>food colouring</u> might contain <u>one dye</u> or it might be a <u>mixture of dyes</u>. Here's how you can tell:

1) <u>Extract</u> the colour from a food sample by placing it in a small cup with a few drops of <u>solvent</u> (can be water, ethanol, salt water, etc).

2) Put <u>spots</u> of the coloured solution on a <u>pencil baseline</u> on filter paper. (Don't use pen because it might dissolve in the solvent and confuse everything.)

3) Roll up the sheet and put it in a <u>beaker</u> with some <u>solvent</u> — but keep the baseline above the level of the solvent.

4) The solvent <u>seeps</u> up the paper, taking the dyes with it. Different dyes form spots in <u>different places</u>.

5) Watch out though — a chromatogram with <u>four spots</u> means <u>at least four</u> dyes, not exactly four dyes. There <u>could</u> be <u>five</u> dyes, with two of them making a spot in the same place. It <u>can't be three</u> dyes though, because one dye can't split into two spots.

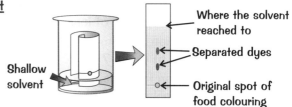

Machines Can Also Analyse Unknown Substances

You can identify elements and compounds using <u>instrumental methods</u> — this just means using machines.

<u>Advantages of Using Machines</u>
- <u>Very sensitive</u> — can detect even the <u>tiniest amounts</u> of substances.
- <u>Very fast</u> and tests can be automated.
- <u>Very accurate</u>

Gas Chromatography Can be Used to Identify Substances

Gas chromatography can <u>separate out</u> a mixture of compounds and help you <u>identify</u> the substances present.

1) A <u>gas</u> is used to <u>carry</u> substances through a <u>column</u> packed with a <u>solid material</u>.

2) The substances travel through the tube at <u>different speeds</u>, so they're <u>separated</u>.

3) The time they take to reach the <u>detector</u> is called the <u>retention time</u>. It can be used to help <u>identify</u> the substances.

4) The recorder draws a <u>gas chromatograph</u>. The number of <u>peaks</u> shows the number of <u>different compounds</u> in the sample.

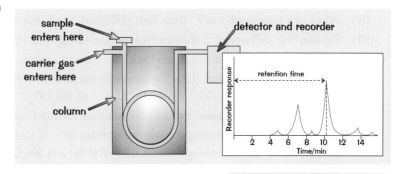

5) The <u>position of the peaks</u> shows the <u>retention time</u> of each substance.

6) The gas chromatography column can also be linked to a <u>mass spectrometer</u>. This process is known as <u>GC-MS</u> and can identify the substances leaving the column very <u>accurately</u>.

7) You can work out the <u>relative molecular mass</u> of each of the substances from the graph it draws. You just <u>read off</u> from the <u>molecular ion peak</u>.

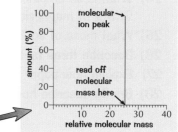

Unfortunately, machines can't do the exam for you...

Make sure you don't get the two types of chromatography muddled up... there's <u>paper</u> and then there's <u>gas</u>.

Revision Summary for Chemistry 2a

Some people skip these pages. But what's the point in reading that great big section if you're not going to check if you really know it or not? Look, just read the first ten questions, and I guarantee there'll be an answer you'll have to look up. And when it comes up in the exam, you'll be so glad you did.

1) What do the mass number and atomic number represent?
2) Draw a table showing the relative masses of the three types of particle in an atom.
3) What is a compound?
4) Define the term isotope.
5) Describe the process of ionic bonding.
6) Describe the structure of a crystal of sodium chloride.
7) List the main properties of ionic compounds.
8) What type of ion do elements from the following groups form?
   a) Group 1   b) Group 7
9)* Use information from the periodic table to help you work out the formulas of these ionic compounds:
   a) potassium chloride   b) calcium chloride
10)* Draw a diagram to show the electronic structure of an Mg^{2+} ion (magnesium's atomic number is 12).
11) What is covalent bonding?
12) Sketch dot and cross diagrams showing the bonding in molecules of:
   a) hydrogen,   b) hydrogen chloride,   c) water,   d) ammonia
13) What are the two types of covalent substance? Give three examples of each.
14) List three properties of metals and explain how metallic bonding causes these properties.
15) Explain why alloys are harder than pure metals.
16)* Identify the structure of each of the substances in the table:

Substance	Melting point (°C)	Electrical conductivity	Hardness [scale of 0 – 10 (10 being diamond)]
A	3410	Very high	7.5
B	2072	Zero	9
C	605	Zero in solid form High when molten	Low

17) Give an example of a "smart" material and describe how it behaves.
18) What are nanoparticles? Give two different applications of nanoparticles.
19) Explain the difference between thermosoftening and thermosetting polymers.
20) Define relative atomic mass and relative formula mass.
21)* Find Ar or Mr for these (use the periodic table at the front of the book):
   a) Ca   b) Ag   c) CO_2 d) $MgCO_3$ e) Na_2CO_3 f) ZnO   g) KOH   h) NH_3
22) What is the link between moles and relative formula mass?
23)*a) Calculate the percentage mass of carbon in: i) $CaCO_3$ ii) CO_2 iii) CH_4
   b) Calculate the percentage mass of metal in: i) Na_2O ii) Fe_2O_3 iii) Al_2O_3
24)*What is an empirical formula? Find the empirical formula of the compound formed when 21.9 g of magnesium, 29.2 g of sulfur and 58.4 g of oxygen react.
25)*What mass of sodium is needed to produce 108.2 g of sodium oxide (Na_2O)?
26) Describe three factors that can reduce the percentage yield of a reaction.
27) Explain how paper chromatography can be used to analyse the dyes used in a brown sweet.
28) Briefly describe how gas chromatography works.

* Answers on page 108.

Rate of Reaction

Reactions can be <u>fast</u> or <u>slow</u> — you've probably already realised that. But you need to know what affects the <u>rate of a reaction</u>, as well as what you can do to <u>measure it</u>. You'll be on the edge of your seat. Honest.

Reactions Can Go at All Sorts of Different Rates

1) One of the <u>slowest</u> is the <u>rusting</u> of iron (it's not slow enough though — what about my little MGB).

2) A <u>moderate speed</u> reaction is a <u>metal</u> (like magnesium) reacting with <u>acid</u> to produce a gentle stream of <u>bubbles</u>.

3) A <u>really fast</u> reaction is an <u>explosion</u>, where it's all over in a <u>fraction</u> of a second.

The Rate of a Reaction Depends on Four Things:

1) <u>Temperature</u>
2) <u>Concentration</u> — (or <u>pressure</u> for gases)
3) <u>Catalyst</u>
4) <u>Surface area of solids</u> — (or <u>size</u> of solid pieces)

LEARN THEM!

Typical Graphs for Rate of Reaction

The plot below shows how the rate of a particular reaction varies under <u>different conditions</u>. The <u>quickest reaction</u> is shown by the line with the <u>steepest slope</u>. Also, the faster a reaction goes, the sooner it finishes, which means that the line becomes <u>flat</u> earlier.

1) <u>Graph 1</u> represents the original <u>fairly slow</u> reaction. The graph is not too steep.

2) <u>Graphs 2 and 3</u> represent the reaction taking place <u>quicker</u> but with the <u>same initial amounts</u>. The slope of the graphs gets steeper.

3) The <u>increased rate</u> could be due to <u>any</u> of these:

   a) increase in <u>temperature</u>
   b) increase in <u>concentration</u> (or pressure)
   c) <u>catalyst</u> added
   d) solid reactant crushed up into <u>smaller bits</u>.

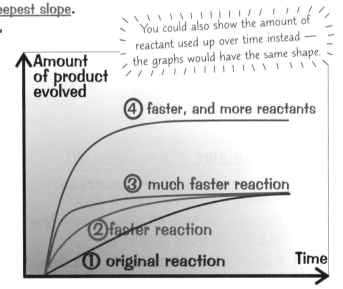

You could also show the amount of reactant used up over time instead — the graphs would have the same shape.

Amount of product evolved

④ faster, and more reactants
③ much faster reaction
② faster reaction
① original reaction

Time

4) <u>Graph 4</u> produces <u>more product</u> as well as going <u>faster</u>. This can <u>only</u> happen if <u>more reactant(s)</u> are added at the start. <u>Graphs 1, 2 and 3</u> all converge at the same level, showing that they all produce the same amount of product, although they take <u>different</u> times to get there.

How to get a fast, furious reaction — crack a wee joke...

<u>Industrial</u> reactions generally use a <u>catalyst</u> and are done at <u>high temperature and pressure</u>. Time is money, so the faster an industrial reaction goes the better... but only <u>up to a point</u>. Chemical plants are quite expensive to rebuild if they get blown into lots and lots of teeny tiny pieces.

Measuring Rates of Reaction

Ways to Measure the Rate of a Reaction

The rate of a reaction can be observed either by measuring how quickly the reactants are used up or how quickly the products are formed. It's usually a lot easier to measure products forming.
The rate of reaction can be calculated using the following formula:

$$\text{Rate of Reaction} = \frac{\text{Amount of reactant used or amount of product formed}}{\text{Time}}$$

There are different ways that the rate of a reaction can be measured. Learn these three:

1) Precipitation

1) This is when the product of the reaction is a precipitate which clouds the solution.
2) Observe a mark through the solution and measure how long it takes for it to disappear.
3) The quicker the mark disappears, the quicker the reaction.
4) This only works for reactions where the initial solution is rather see-through.
5) The result is very subjective — different people might not agree over the exact point when the mark 'disappears'.

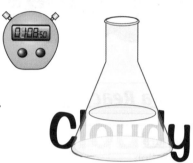

2) Change in Mass (Usually Gas Given Off)

1) Measuring the speed of a reaction that produces a gas can be carried out on a mass balance.
2) As the gas is released the mass disappearing is easily measured on the balance.
3) The quicker the reading on the balance drops, the faster the reaction.
4) Rate of reaction graphs are particularly easy to plot using the results from this method.
5) This is the most accurate of the three methods described on this page because the mass balance is very accurate. But it has the disadvantage of releasing the gas straight into the room.

3) The Volume of Gas Given Off

1) This involves the use of a gas syringe to measure the volume of gas given off.
2) The more gas given off during a given time interval, the faster the reaction.
3) A graph of gas volume against time elapsed could be plotted to give a rate of reaction graph.
4) Gas syringes usually give volumes accurate to the nearest millilitre, so they're quite accurate. You have to be quite careful though — if the reaction is too vigorous, you can easily blow the plunger out of the end of the syringe!

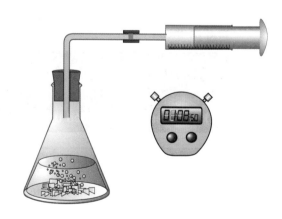

OK have you got your stopwatch ready *BANG!* — oh...

Each method has its pros and cons. The mass balance method is only accurate as long as the flask isn't too hot, otherwise you lose mass by evaporation as well as by the reaction. The first method isn't very accurate, but if you're not producing a gas you can't use either of the other two. Ah well.

Rate of Reaction Experiments

Remember: <u>Any reaction</u> can be used to investigate <u>any</u> of the four factors that affect the <u>rate</u>. These pages illustrate <u>four important reactions</u>, but only <u>one factor</u> has been considered for each. But we could just as easily use, say, the marble chips/acid reaction to test the effect of <u>temperature</u> instead.

1) Reaction of Hydrochloric Acid and Marble Chips

This experiment is often used to demonstrate the effect of <u>breaking</u> the solid up into <u>small bits</u>.

1) Measure the <u>volume</u> of gas evolved with a <u>gas syringe</u> and take readings at <u>regular intervals</u>.

2) Make a <u>table of readings</u> and plot them as a <u>graph</u>. You <u>choose</u> regular time intervals, and <u>time</u> goes on the <u>x-axis</u> and <u>volume</u> goes on the <u>y-axis</u>.

3) <u>Repeat</u> the experiment with <u>exactly the same</u> volume of <u>acid</u>, and <u>exactly the same</u> mass of <u>marble</u> chips, but with the marble <u>more crunched up</u>.

4) Then <u>repeat</u> with the same mass of <u>powdered chalk</u> instead of marble chips.

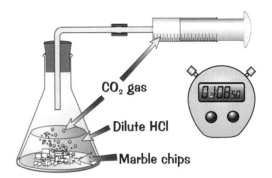

CO$_2$ gas
Dilute HCl
Marble chips

This graph shows the effect of using finer particles of solid

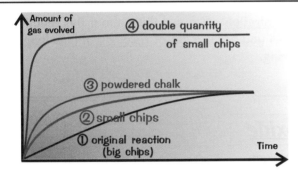

④ double quantity of small chips
③ powdered chalk
② small chips
① original reaction (big chips)
Amount of gas evolved
Time

1) Using <u>finer particles</u> means that the marble has a <u>larger surface area</u>.

2) A larger <u>surface area</u> causes <u>more frequent collisions</u> (see page 59) so the rate of reaction is <u>faster</u>.

3) <u>Line 4</u> shows the reaction if a <u>greater mass</u> of small marble chips is added. The <u>extra surface area</u> gives a <u>quicker reaction</u> and there is also <u>more gas evolved</u> overall.

2) Reaction of Magnesium Metal with Dilute HCl

1) <u>This reaction</u> is good for measuring the effects of <u>increased concentration</u> (as is the marble/acid reaction).

2) This reaction gives off <u>hydrogen gas</u>, which we can measure with a <u>mass balance</u>, as shown.

3) In this experiment, <u>time</u> also goes on the <u>x-axis</u> and <u>volume</u> goes on the <u>y-axis</u>.

(The other method is to use a gas syringe, as above.)

This graph shows the effect of using more concentrated acid solutions

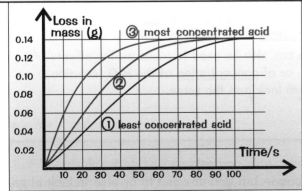

Loss in mass (g)
③ most concentrated acid
②
① least concentrated acid
Time/s
10 20 30 40 50 60 70 80 90 100
0.14 0.12 0.10 0.08 0.06 0.04 0.02

1) Take <u>readings</u> of mass at <u>regular</u> time intervals.

2) Put the results in a <u>table</u> and work out the <u>loss in mass</u> for each reading. <u>Plot a graph</u>.

3) <u>Repeat</u> with <u>more concentrated</u> acid solutions, but always with the <u>same</u> amount of magnesium.

4) The <u>volume</u> of acid must always be kept <u>the same</u> too — only the <u>concentration</u> is increased.

5) The three graphs show the <u>same</u> old pattern — a <u>higher</u> concentration giving a <u>steeper graph</u>, with the reaction <u>finishing</u> much quicker.

More Rate of Reaction Experiments

3) Sodium Thiosulfate and HCl Produce a Cloudy Precipitate

1) These two chemicals are both <u>clear solutions</u>.

2) They react together to form a <u>yellow precipitate</u> of <u>sulfur</u>.

3) The experiment involves watching a black mark <u>disappear</u> through the <u>cloudy sulfur</u> and <u>timing</u> how long it takes to go.

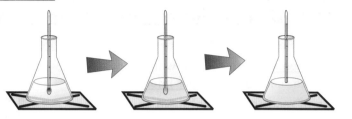

4) The reaction can be <u>repeated</u> for solutions at different <u>temperatures</u>. In practice, that's quite hard to do accurately and safely (it's not a good idea to heat an acid directly). The best way to do it is to use a <u>water bath</u> to heat both solutions to the right temperature <u>before you mix them</u>.

5) The <u>depth</u> of liquid must be kept the <u>same</u> each time, of course.

6) The results will of course show that the <u>higher</u> the temperature the <u>quicker</u> the reaction and therefore the <u>less time</u> it takes for the mark to <u>disappear</u>. These are typical results:

Temperature (°C)	20	25	30	35	40
Time taken for mark to disappear (s)	193	151	112	87	52

This reaction can <u>also</u> be used to test the effects of <u>concentration</u>. One sad thing about this reaction is it <u>doesn't</u> give a set of graphs. Well I think it's sad. All you get is a set of <u>readings</u> of how long it took till the mark disappeared for each temperature. Boring.

4) The Decomposition of Hydrogen Peroxide

This is a <u>good</u> reaction for showing the effect of different <u>catalysts</u>. The decomposition of hydrogen peroxide is:

$$2H_2O_{2(aq)} \rightarrow 2H_2O_{(l)} + O_{2(g)}$$

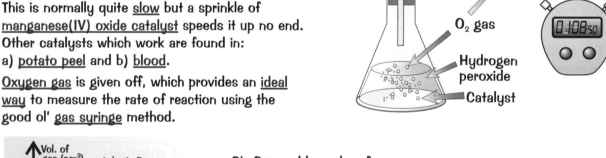

1) This is normally quite <u>slow</u> but a sprinkle of <u>manganese(IV) oxide catalyst</u> speeds it up no end. Other catalysts which work are found in:
a) <u>potato peel</u> and b) <u>blood</u>.

2) <u>Oxygen gas</u> is given off, which provides an <u>ideal way</u> to measure the rate of reaction using the good ol' <u>gas syringe</u> method.

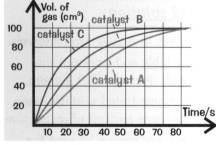

3) Same old graphs of course.

4) <u>Better</u> catalysts give a <u>quicker reaction</u>, which is shown by a <u>steeper graph</u> which levels off quickly.

5) This reaction can also be used to measure the effects of <u>temperature</u>, or of <u>concentration</u> of the H_2O_2 solution. The graphs will look just the same.

BLOOD is a catalyst? — eeurgh...

You don't need to know all the details of these specific reactions — but you do need to be able to look at graphs showing the amount of product formed (or reactant used up) over time and comment on the reaction rate.

Collision Theory

Reaction rates are explained by collision theory. It's really simple. It just says that the rate of a reaction simply depends on how often and how hard the reacting particles collide with each other. The basic idea is that particles have to collide in order to react, and they have to collide hard enough (with enough energy).

More Collisions Increases the Rate of Reaction

The effects of temperature, concentration and surface area on the rate of reaction can be explained in terms of how often the reacting particles collide successfully.

1) HIGHER TEMPERATURE increases collisions

When the temperature is increased the particles all move quicker.
If they're moving quicker, they're going to collide more often.

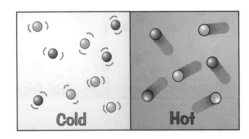

2) HIGHER CONCENTRATION (or PRESSURE) increases collisions

If a solution is made more concentrated it means there are more particles of reactant knocking about between the water molecules which makes collisions between the important particles more likely.

In a gas, increasing the pressure means the particles are more squashed up together so there will be more frequent collisions.

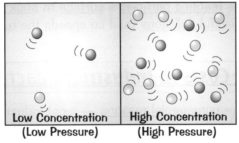

3) LARGER SURFACE AREA increases collisions

If one of the reactants is a solid then breaking it up into smaller pieces will increase the total surface area. This means the particles around it in the solution will have more area to work on, so there'll be more frequent collisions.

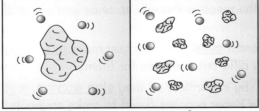

Collision theory — the lamppost ran into me...

Once you've learnt everything off this page, the rates of reaction stuff should start making a lot more sense to you. Isn't it nice when everything starts to fall into place... The concept's fairly simple — the more often particles bump into each other, and the harder they hit when they do, the faster the reaction happens.

Collision Theory and Catalysts

Without enough <u>activation energy</u>, it's game over before you start.

Faster Collisions Increase the Rate of Reaction

<u>Higher temperature</u> also increases the <u>energy</u> of the collisions, because it makes all the particles <u>move faster</u>.

Increasing the temperature causes faster collisions

Reactions <u>only happen</u> if the particles collide with <u>enough energy</u>.

The <u>minimum amount</u> of energy needed by the particles to react is known as the <u>activation energy</u>.

At a <u>higher temperature</u> there will be <u>more particles</u> colliding with <u>enough energy</u> to make the reaction happen.

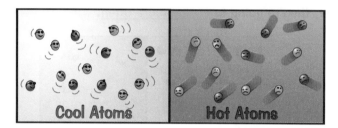

Cool Atoms   Hot Atoms

Catalysts Speed Up Reactions

Many reactions can be <u>speeded up</u> by adding a <u>catalyst</u>.

A <u>catalyst</u> is a substance which <u>speeds up</u> a reaction, without being <u>changed</u> or <u>used up</u> in the reaction.

A <u>solid catalyst</u> works by giving the <u>reacting particles</u> a <u>surface</u> to <u>stick to</u>.
This increases the number of <u>successful collisions</u> (and so speeds the reaction up).

Catalysts Help Reduce Costs in Industrial Reactions

1) Catalysts are <u>very important</u> for <u>commercial reasons</u> — most industrial reactions use them.

2) <u>Catalysts</u> increase the rate of the reaction, which saves a lot of <u>money</u> simply because the plant doesn't need to operate for <u>as long</u> to produce the <u>same amount</u> of stuff.

3) Alternatively, a catalyst will allow the reaction to work at a <u>much lower temperature</u>. That reduces the <u>energy</u> used up in the reaction (the <u>energy cost</u>), which is good for <u>sustainable development</u> (see page 52) and can save a lot of money too.

4) There are <u>disadvantages</u> to using catalysts, though.

5) They can be very expensive to buy, and often need to be removed from the product and cleaned. They never get <u>used up</u> in the reaction though, so once you've got them you can use them <u>over and over</u> again.

6) Different <u>reactions</u> use different <u>catalysts</u>, so if you make <u>more than one product</u> at your plant, you'll probably need to buy different catalysts for them.

7) Catalysts can be '<u>poisoned</u>' by impurities, so they <u>stop working</u>, e.g. sulfur impurities can poison the iron catalyst used in the Haber process (used to make ammonia for fertilisers). That means you have to keep your reaction mixture very <u>clean</u>.

Catalysts are like great jokes — they can be used over and over...

And they're not only used in <u>industry</u>... every useful chemical reaction in the human body is catalysed by a <u>biological catalyst</u> (an enzyme). If the reactions in the body were just left to their own devices, they'd take so long to happen, we couldn't exist. Quite handy then, these catalysts.

Energy Transfer in Reactions

Whenever chemical reactions occur <u>energy</u> is <u>transferred to</u> or <u>from</u> the <u>surroundings</u>.

In an <u>Exothermic</u> Reaction, Heat is <u>Given Out</u>

> An <u>EXOTHERMIC reaction</u> is one which <u>transfers energy</u> to the surroundings, usually in the form of <u>heat</u> and usually shown by a <u>rise in temperature.</u>

1) The best example of an <u>exothermic</u> reaction is <u>burning fuels</u> — also called <u>COMBUSTION</u>. This gives out a lot of heat — it's very exothermic.

2) <u>Neutralisation reactions</u> (acid + alkali) are also exothermic — see page 62.

3) Many <u>oxidation reactions</u> are exothermic. For example, adding sodium to water <u>produces heat</u>, so it must be <u>exothermic</u>. The sodium emits <u>heat</u> and moves about on the surface of the water as it is oxidised.

4) Exothermic reactions have lots of <u>everyday uses</u>. For example, some <u>hand warmers</u> use the exothermic <u>oxidation of iron</u> in air (with a salt solution catalyst) to generate <u>heat</u>. <u>Self heating cans</u> of hot chocolate and coffee also rely on exothermic reactions between <u>chemicals</u> in their bases.

In an <u>Endothermic</u> Reaction, Heat is <u>Taken In</u>

> An <u>ENDOTHERMIC reaction</u> is one which <u>takes in energy</u> from the surroundings, usually in the form of <u>heat</u> and is usually shown by a <u>fall in temperature.</u>

Endothermic reactions are much <u>less common</u>. <u>Thermal decompositions</u> are a good example:

> Heat must be supplied to make calcium carbonate <u>decompose</u> to make quicklime.
> $$CaCO_3 \quad \rightarrow \quad CaO + CO_2$$

Endothermic reactions also have everyday uses. For example, some <u>sports injury packs</u> use endothermic reactions — they <u>take in heat</u> and the pack becomes very <u>cold</u>. More <u>convenient</u> than carrying ice around.

<u>Reversible Reactions</u> Can Be <u>Endothermic</u> and <u>Exothermic</u>

In reversible reactions (see page 52), if the reaction is <u>endothermic</u> in <u>one direction</u>, it will be <u>exothermic</u> in the <u>other direction</u>. The <u>energy absorbed</u> by the endothermic reaction is <u>equal</u> to the <u>energy released</u> during the exothermic reaction. A good example is the <u>thermal decomposition of hydrated copper sulfate</u>.

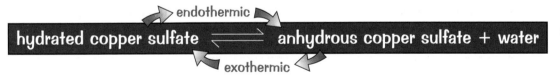

"Anhydrous" just means "without water", and "hydrated" means "with water".

1) If you <u>heat blue hydrated</u> copper(II) sulfate crystals it drives the water off and leaves <u>white anhydrous</u> copper(II) sulfate powder. This is endothermic.

Water vapour

2) If you then <u>add</u> a couple of drops of <u>water</u> to the <u>white powder</u> you get the <u>blue crystals</u> back again. This is exothermic.

<u>Right, so burning gives out heat — really...</u>

This whole energy transfer thing is a fairly simple idea — don't be put off by the long words.
Remember, "<u>exo-</u>" = <u>exit</u>, "<u>-thermic</u>" = <u>heat</u>, so an exothermic reaction is one that <u>gives out</u> heat.
And "<u>endo-</u>" = erm... the other one. Okay, so there's no easy way to remember that one. Tough.

Acids and Alkalis

Testing the pH of a solution means using an <u>indicator</u> — and that means pretty <u>colours</u>...

The pH Scale Goes From 0 to 14

1) The <u>pH scale</u> is a measure of how <u>acidic</u> or <u>alkaline</u> a solution is.
2) The <u>strongest acid</u> has <u>pH 0</u>. The <u>strongest alkali</u> has <u>pH 14</u>.
3) A <u>neutral</u> substance has <u>pH 7</u> (e.g. pure water).

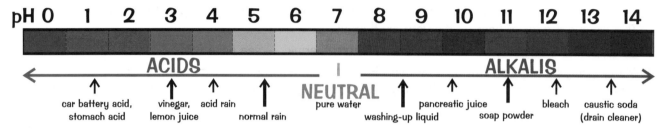

An Indicator is Just a Dye That Changes Colour

The dye in the indicator <u>changes colour</u> depending on whether it's <u>above or below a certain pH</u>. <u>Universal indicator</u> is a <u>combination of dyes</u> which gives the colours shown above.

It's very useful for <u>estimating</u> the pH of a solution.

Acids and Bases Neutralise Each Other

> An <u>ACID</u> is a substance with a pH of less than 7. Acids form <u>H^+ ions</u> in <u>water</u>.
> A <u>BASE</u> is a substance with a pH of greater than 7.
> An <u>ALKALI</u> is a base that <u>dissolves in water</u>. Alkalis form <u>OH^- ions</u> in <u>water</u>.
> So, <u>H^+</u> ions make solutions <u>acidic</u> and <u>OH^-</u> ions make them <u>alkaline</u>.

The reaction between acids and bases is called <u>neutralisation</u>. Make sure you learn it:

$$ \text{acid} + \text{base} \rightarrow \text{salt} + \text{water} $$

Neutralisation can also be seen in terms of <u>H^+</u> and <u>OH^- ions</u> like this, so learn it too:

$$ H^+_{(aq)} + OH^-_{(aq)} \rightarrow H_2O_{(l)} $$

Hydrogen (H^+) ions react with hydroxide (OH^-) ions to produce water.

When an acid neutralises a base (or vice versa), the <u>products</u> are <u>neutral</u>, i.e. they have a <u>pH of 7</u>. An indicator can be used to show that a neutralisation reaction is over (Universal indicator will go green).

State Symbols Tell You What Physical State It's In

These are easy enough, <u>so make sure you know them</u> — especially aq (aqueous).

(s) — Solid	(l) — Liquid	(g) — Gas	(aq) — Dissolved in water

E.g. $2Mg_{(s)} + O_{2(g)} \rightarrow 2MgO_{(s)}$

Interesting(ish) fact — your skin is slightly acidic (pH 5.5)...

The neutralisation reaction's a great one to know. If you have <u>indigestion</u>, it's because you've got too much hydrochloric acid in your stomach. Indigestion tablets contain bases that neutralise some of the acid.

Acids Reacting With Metals

Sadly, the <u>salts</u> on this page aren't the sort you'd want to go putting on your fish 'n' chips.

Metals *React With Acids to Give Salts*

Acid + Metal → Salt + Hydrogen

That's written big 'cos it's kinda worth remembering.   Here's the <u>typical experiment</u>:

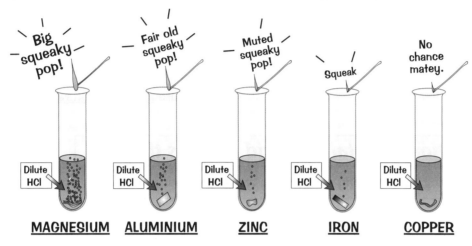

MAGNESIUM   ALUMINIUM   ZINC   IRON   COPPER

1) The more <u>reactive</u> the metal, the <u>faster</u> the reaction will go — very reactive metals (e.g. sodium) react <u>explosively</u>.

2) <u>Copper</u> does <u>not</u> react with dilute acids <u>at all</u> — because it's <u>less</u> reactive than <u>hydrogen</u>.

3) The <u>speed</u> of reaction is indicated by the <u>rate</u> at which the <u>bubbles</u> of hydrogen are given off.

4) The <u>hydrogen</u> is confirmed by the <u>burning splint test</u> giving the notorious '<u>squeaky pop</u>'.

5) The <u>name</u> of the <u>salt</u> produced depends on which <u>metal</u> is used, and which <u>acid</u> is used:

Hydrochloric Acid Will Always Produce Chloride Salts:

$2HCl + Mg \rightarrow MgCl_2 + H_2$ (Magnesium chloride)

$6HCl + 2Al \rightarrow 2AlCl_3 + 3H_2$ (Aluminium chloride)

$2HCl + Zn \rightarrow ZnCl_2 + H_2$ (Zinc chloride)

Sulfuric Acid Will Always Produce Sulfate Salts:

$H_2SO_4 + Mg \rightarrow MgSO_4 + H_2$ (Magnesium sulfate)

$3H_2SO_4 + 2Al \rightarrow Al_2(SO_4)_3 + 3H_2$ (Aluminium sulfate)

$H_2SO_4 + Zn \rightarrow ZnSO_4 + H_2$ (Zinc sulfate)

Nitric Acid Produces Nitrate Salts When NEUTRALISED, But...

Nitric acid reacts fine with alkalis, to produce nitrates, but it can play silly devils with metals and produce nitrogen oxides instead, so we'll ignore it here. Chemistry's a real messy subject sometimes, innit.

Nitric acid, tut — there's always one...

Okay, so this stuff isn't exactly a laugh a minute, but at least it's fairly straightforward learning. Metals that are <u>less</u> reactive than <u>hydrogen</u> don't react with acid, and some metals like sodium and potassium are <u>too</u> reactive to mix with acid in a school lab — your beaker would <u>explode</u>.

Oxides, Hydroxides and Ammonia

I'm afraid there's more stuff on <u>neutralisation</u> reactions coming up...

Metal <u>Oxides</u> and Metal <u>Hydroxides</u> <u>Are</u> <u>Bases</u>

1) Some <u>metal oxides</u> and <u>metal hydroxides</u> dissolve in <u>water</u>. These soluble compounds are <u>alkalis</u>.

2) Even bases that won't dissolve in water will still react with acids.

3) So, all <u>metal oxides</u> and <u>metal hydroxides</u> react with <u>acids</u> to form a <u>salt</u> and <u>water</u>.

> **Acid + Metal Oxide → Salt + Water**

> **Acid + Metal Hydroxide → Salt + Water**

(These are <u>neutralisation reactions</u> of course)

The <u>Combination</u> of Metal and Acid Decides the <u>Salt</u>

This isn't exactly exciting but it's pretty easy, so try and get the hang of it:

hydrochloric acid	+	copper oxide	→	copper chloride + water
hydrochloric acid	+	sodium hydroxide	→	sodium chloride + water
sulfuric acid	+	zinc oxide	→	zinc sulfate + water
sulfuric acid	+	calcium hydroxide	→	calcium sulfate + water
nitric acid	+	magnesium oxide	→	magnesium nitrate + water
nitric acid	+	potassium hydroxide	→	potassium nitrate + water

The symbol equations are all pretty much the same. Here are two of them:

$$H_2SO_{4\ (aq)} + ZnO_{(s)} \rightarrow ZnSO_{4\ (aq)} + H_2O_{(l)}$$
$$HNO_{3\ (aq)} + KOH_{(aq)} \rightarrow KNO_{3\ (aq)} + H_2O_{(l)}$$

Ammonia Can Be <u>Neutralised</u> with HNO$_3$ to Make <u>Fertiliser</u>

<u>Ammonia</u> dissolves in water to make an <u>alkaline solution</u>.
When it reacts with <u>nitric acid</u>, you get a <u>neutral salt</u> — <u>ammonium nitrate</u>:

$$NH_{3\ (aq)} + HNO_{3\ (aq)} \rightarrow NH_4NO_{3\ (aq)}$$
Ammonia + Nitric acid → Ammonium nitrate

This is a bit different from most neutralisation reactions because there's <u>NO WATER</u> produced — just the ammonium salt.

<u>Ammonium nitrate</u> is an especially good fertiliser because it has <u>nitrogen</u> from <u>two sources</u>, the ammonia and the nitric acid. Kind of a <u>double dose</u>. Plants need nitrogen to make <u>proteins</u>.

<u>There's nowt wrong wi' just spreadin' muck on it...</u>

Not the most thrilling of pages, I'm afraid. Just loads of reactions for you to learn. Try doing different combinations of acids and alkalis. <u>Balance</u> them. Cover the page and scribble all the equations down. If you make any mistakes... <u>learn</u> it again, <u>cover</u> it up again, and <u>scribble</u> it all down again.

Making Salts

If you're making a salt it's important to know if it's soluble or not so you know which method to use. Most chlorides, sulfates and nitrates are soluble in water (the main exceptions are lead chloride, lead sulfate and silver chloride). Most oxides and hydroxides are insoluble in water.

Making Soluble Salts Using a Metal or an Insoluble Base

1) You need to pick the right acid, plus a metal or an insoluble base (a metal oxide or metal hydroxide). E.g. if you want to make copper chloride, mix hydrochloric acid and copper oxide.

Remember some metals are unreactive and others are too reactive to use for this reaction (see page 63).

E.g. $CuO_{(s)} + 2HCl_{(aq)} \longrightarrow CuCl_{2\,(aq)} + H_2O_{(l)}$

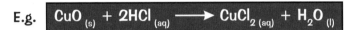

2) You add the metal, metal oxide or hydroxide to the acid — the solid will dissolve in the acid as it reacts. You will know when all the acid has been neutralised because the excess solid will just sink to the bottom of the flask.

3) Then filter out the excess metal, metal oxide or metal hydroxide to get the salt solution. To get pure, solid crystals of the salt, evaporate some of the water (to make the solution more concentrated) and then leave the rest to evaporate very slowly. This is called crystallisation.

Making Soluble Salts Using an Alkali

1) You can't use the method above with alkalis (soluble bases) like sodium, potassium or ammonium hydroxides, because you can't tell whether the reaction has finished — you can't just add an excess to the acid and filter out what's left.

2) You have to add exactly the right amount of alkali to just neutralise the acid — you need to use an indicator (see page 62) to show when the reaction's finished. Then repeat using exactly the same volumes of alkali and acid so the salt isn't contaminated with indicator.

3) Then just evaporate off the water to crystallise the salt as normal.

Making Insoluble Salts — Precipitation Reactions

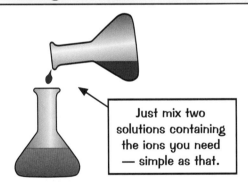

Just mix two solutions containing the ions you need — simple as that.

1) If the salt you want to make is insoluble, you can use a precipitation reaction.

2) You just need to pick two solutions that contain the ions you need. E.g. to make lead chloride you need a solution which contains lead ions and one which contains chloride ions. So you can mix lead nitrate solution (most nitrates are soluble) with sodium chloride solution (all group 1 compounds are soluble).

E.g. $Pb(NO_3)_{2\,(aq)} + 2NaCl_{(aq)} \longrightarrow PbCl_{2\,(s)} + 2NaNO_{3\,(aq)}$

3) Once the salt has precipitated out (and is lying at the bottom of your flask), all you have to do is filter it from the solution, wash it and then dry it on filter paper.

4) Precipitation reactions can be used to remove poisonous ions (e.g. lead) from drinking water. Calcium and magnesium ions can also be removed from water this way — they make water "hard", which stops soap lathering properly. Another use of precipitation is in treating effluent (sewage) — again, unwanted ions can be removed.

Get two beakers, mix 'em together — job's a good'n...

In the exam, you could be asked to describe how to make a given soluble or insoluble salt. You need to think carefully about what chemicals you'd need to get the salt you want and what method you'd use.

Electrolysis

Hmm, electrolysis. A not-very-catchy title for quite a <u>sparky</u> subject...

Electrolysis Means "Splitting Up with Electricity"

1) If you pass an <u>electric current</u> through an <u>ionic substance</u> that's <u>molten</u> or in <u>solution</u>, it breaks down into the <u>elements</u> it's made of. This is called <u>electrolysis</u>.

2) It requires a <u>liquid</u> to <u>conduct</u> the <u>electricity</u>, called the <u>electrolyte</u>.

3) Electrolytes contain <u>free ions</u> — they're usually the <u>molten</u> or <u>dissolved ionic substance</u>.

4) In either case it's the <u>free ions</u> which <u>conduct</u> the electricity and allow the whole thing to work.

5) For an electrical circuit to be complete, there's got to be a <u>flow of electrons</u>. <u>Electrons</u> are taken <u>away from</u> ions at the <u>positive electrode</u> and <u>given to</u> other ions at the <u>negative electrode</u>. As ions gain or lose electrons they become atoms or molecules and are released.

NaCl dissolved

Molten NaCl

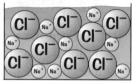

Electrolysis Reactions Involve <u>Oxidation</u> and <u>Reduction</u>

1) Back in Core Chemistry you learnt about <u>reduction</u> involving the <u>loss of oxygen</u>. However...

2) <u>Reduction</u> is also a <u>gain of electrons</u>.

3) On the other hand, <u>oxidation</u> is a gain of oxygen or a <u>loss of electrons</u>.

4) So "reduction" and "oxidation" don't have to involve <u>oxygen</u>.

5) Electrolysis <u>ALWAYS</u> involves an oxidation and a reduction.

Oxidation Is Loss	Reduction Is Gain

Remember it as OIL RIG.

The <u>Electrolysis</u> of Molten <u>Lead Bromide</u>

When a salt (e.g. lead bromide) is molten it will conduct electricity.

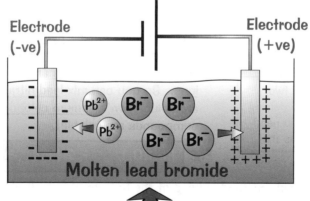

<u>+ve ions</u> are attracted to the <u>-ve electrode</u>. Here they <u>gain electrons</u> (reduction).	Electrode (-ve) Electrode (+ve) HEAT Molten lead bromide	<u>-ve ions</u> are attracted to the <u>+ve electrode</u>. Here they <u>lose electrons</u> (oxidation).

<u>Lead</u> is produced at the <u>-ve electrode</u>.

<u>Bromine</u> is produced at the <u>+ve electrode</u>.

1) At the <u>-ve electrode</u>, one lead ion <u>accepts</u> two electrons to become <u>one lead atom</u>.

2) At the <u>+ve electrode</u>, two bromide ions <u>lose</u> one electron each and become <u>one bromine molecule</u>.

Faster shopping at Tesco — use Electrolleys...

Learn the <u>products</u> of the electrolysis of molten lead bromide and make sure you know which is <u>oxidation</u> and which is <u>reduction</u>. Electrolysis is used lots in <u>real life</u>, and it's nice to know how these things work, I reckon.

Electrolysis of Sodium Chloride Solution

As well as <u>molten substances</u> you can also electrolyse <u>solutions</u>. But first, a bit more about the <u>products</u>...

Reactivity Affects the Products Formed By Electrolysis

1) Sometimes there are <u>more than two free ions</u> in the electrolyte.
   For example, if a salt is <u>dissolved in water</u> there will also be some <u>H⁺</u> and <u>OH⁻</u> ions.

2) At the <u>negative electrode</u>, if <u>metal ions</u> and <u>H⁺ ions</u> are present, the metal ions will <u>stay in solution</u> if the metal is <u>more reactive</u> than hydrogen. This is because the more reactive an element, the keener it is to stay as ions. So, <u>hydrogen</u> will be produced unless the metal is <u>less reactive</u> than it.

3) At the <u>positive electrode</u>, if <u>OH⁻</u> and <u>halide ions</u> (Cl⁻, Br⁻, I⁻) are present then molecules of chlorine, bromine or iodine will be formed. If <u>no halide</u> is present, then <u>oxygen</u> will be formed.

The Electrolysis of Sodium Chloride Solution

When common salt (sodium chloride) is dissolved in water and electrolysed,
it produces three useful products — <u>hydrogen</u>, <u>chlorine</u> and <u>sodium hydroxide</u>.

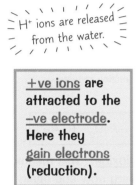

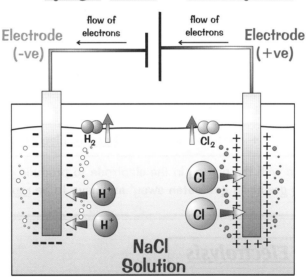

+ve ions are attracted to the −ve electrode. Here they gain electrons (reduction).

<u>Hydrogen</u> is produced at the <u>−ve electrode</u>.

−ve ions are attracted to the +ve electrode. Here they lose electrons (oxidation).

<u>Chlorine</u> is produced at the <u>+ve electrode</u>.

1) At the <u>negative electrode</u>, two hydrogen ions accept two electrons to become <u>one hydrogen molecule</u>.

2) At the <u>positive electrode</u>, two chloride (Cl⁻) ions lose their electrons and become <u>one chlorine molecule</u>.

3) The <u>sodium ions</u> stay in solution because they're <u>more reactive</u> than hydrogen. <u>Hydroxide ions</u> from water are also left behind. This means that <u>sodium hydroxide</u> (NaOH) is left in the solution.

The Half-Equations — Make Sure the Electrons Balance

Half equations show the reactions at the electrodes. The main thing is to make sure the <u>number of electrons</u> is the <u>same</u> for <u>both half-equations</u>. For the electrolysis of sodium chloride the half-equations are:

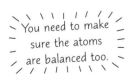

Negative Electrode: $2H^+ + 2e^- \rightarrow H_2$
Positive Electrode: $2Cl^- \rightarrow Cl_2 + 2e^-$
or $2Cl^- - 2e^- \rightarrow Cl_2$

For the electrolysis of molten lead bromide (previous page) the half equations would be:
$Pb^{2+} + 2e^- \rightarrow Pb$
and $2Br^- \rightarrow Br_2 + 2e^-$

Useful Products from the Electrolysis of Sodium Chloride Solution

The products of the electrolysis of sodium chloride solution are pretty useful in <u>industry</u>.
1) Chlorine has many uses, e.g. in the production of <u>bleach</u> and <u>plastics</u>.
2) Sodium hydroxide is a very strong <u>alkali</u> and is used <u>widely</u> in the <u>chemical industry</u>, e.g. to make <u>soap</u>.

Extraction of Aluminium and Electroplating

I bet you never thought you'd <u>need to know so much</u> about electrolysis — but, sadly, <u>you do</u>. So get reading this lot...

Electrolysis <u>is</u> Used to Remove Aluminium <u>from Its</u> Ore

1) Aluminium's a very <u>abundant</u> metal, but it is always found naturally in <u>compounds</u>.
2) Its main ore is <u>bauxite</u>, and after mining and purifying, a <u>white powder</u> is left.
3) This is <u>pure</u> aluminium oxide, Al_2O_3.
4) The <u>aluminium</u> has to be extracted from this using <u>electrolysis</u>.

Cryolite <u>is Used to</u> Lower <u>the Temperature (and Costs)</u>

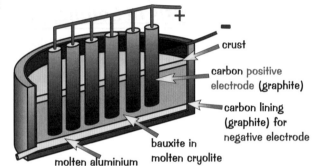

1) Al_2O_3 has a very <u>high melting point</u> of over <u>2000 °C</u> — so melting it would be very <u>expensive</u>.
2) <u>Instead</u> the aluminium oxide is <u>dissolved</u> in <u>molten cryolite</u> (a less common ore of aluminium).
3) This brings the <u>temperature down</u> to about <u>900 °C</u>, which makes it much <u>cheaper</u> and <u>easier</u>.
4) The <u>electrodes</u> are made of <u>carbon</u> (graphite), a good conductor of electricity (see page 45).
5) <u>Aluminium</u> forms at the <u>negative electrode</u> and <u>oxygen</u> forms at the <u>positive electrode</u>.

crust
carbon positive electrode (graphite)
carbon lining (graphite) for negative electrode
bauxite in molten cryolite
molten aluminium

<u>Negative Electrode</u>: $Al^{3+} + 3e^- \rightarrow Al$ <u>Positive Electrode</u>: $2O^{2-} \rightarrow O_2 + 4e^-$

6) The <u>oxygen</u> then reacts with the <u>carbon</u> in the electrode to produce <u>carbon dioxide</u>. This means that the <u>positive electrodes</u> gradually get 'eaten away' and have to be <u>replaced</u> every now and again.

Electroplating <u>Uses Electrolysis</u>

1) Electroplating uses electrolysis to <u>coat</u> the <u>surface of one metal</u> with <u>another metal</u>, e.g. you might want to electroplate silver onto a brass cup to make it look nice.
2) The <u>negative electrode</u> is the <u>metal object</u> you want to plate and the <u>positive electrode</u> is the <u>pure metal</u> you want it to be plated with. You also need the <u>electrolyte</u> to contain ions of the <u>plating metal</u>. (The ions that plate the metal object come from the solution, while the positive electrode keeps the solution 'topped up'.)

<u>Example</u>: To electroplate <u>silver</u> onto a <u>brass cup</u>, you'd make the <u>brass cup</u> the negative electrode (to attract the positive silver ions), a lump of <u>pure silver</u> the positive electrode and dip them in a solution of <u>silver ions</u>, e.g. silver nitrate.

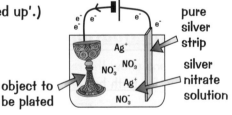

pure silver strip
silver nitrate solution
object to be plated

3) There are lots of different <u>uses</u> for electroplating:
- <u>Decoration</u>: <u>Silver</u> is <u>attractive</u>, but very <u>expensive</u>. It's much <u>cheaper</u> to plate a boring brass cup with silver, than it is to make the cup out of solid silver — but it looks just as <u>pretty</u>.
- <u>Conduction</u>: Metals like <u>copper</u> conduct <u>electricity</u> well — because of this they're often used to plate metals for <u>electronic circuits</u> and <u>computers</u>.

Silver electroplated text is worth a fortune...

There are loads of metals you can use for electroplating, but you just need to know about silver and copper plating. The tricky bit is remembering that the metal <u>object you want to plate</u> is the <u>negative electrode</u> and the <u>metal</u> you're plating it with is the <u>positive electrode</u>. Oh, and don't forget to learn about aluminium electrolysis.

Revision Summary for Chemistry 2b

Well, I don't think that was too bad, was it... Four things affect the rate of reactions, there are loads of ways to measure reaction rates and it's all explained by collision theory. Reactions can be endothermic or exothermic, and quite a few of them are reversible. And so on... Easy. Ahem.
Well here are some more of those nice questions that you enjoy so much. If there are any you can't answer, go back to the appropriate page, do a bit more learning, then try again.

1) What are the four factors that affect the rate of a reaction?
2) Describe three different ways of measuring the rate of a reaction.
3) A student carries out an experiment to measure the effect of surface area on the reaction between marble and hydrochloric acid. He measures the amount of gas given off at regular intervals.
   a) What factors must he keep constant for it to be a fair test?
   b)* He uses four samples for his experiment:
      Sample A – 10 g of powdered marble
      Sample B – 10 g of small marble chips
      Sample C – 10 g of large marble chips
      Sample D – 5 g of powdered marble
   Sketch a typical set of graphs for this experiment.
4) Explain how higher temperature, higher concentration and larger surface area increase the frequency of successful collisions between particles.
5) What is activation energy?
6) What is the definition of a catalyst?
7) Discuss the advantages and disadvantages of using catalysts in industrial processes.
8) What is an exothermic reaction? Give three examples.
9) The reaction to split ammonium chloride into ammonia and hydrogen chloride is endothermic. What can you say for certain about the reverse reaction?
10) What does the pH scale show?
11) What type of ions are always present in a) acids and   b) alkalis?
12) What is neutralisation? Write down the general equation for neutralisation in terms of ions.
13) Write down the state symbol that means 'dissolved in water'.
14) What is the general equation for reacting an acid with a metal?
15) Name a metal that doesn't react at all with dilute acids.
16) What type of salts do hydrochloric acid and sulfuric acid produce?
17) What type of reaction is "acid + metal oxide", or "acid + metal hydroxide"?
18) Write a balanced symbol equation for the reaction between ammonia and nitric acid. What is the product of this reaction useful for?
19) Suggest a suitable acid and a suitable metal oxide/hydroxide to mix to form the following salts.
   a) copper chloride   b) calcium nitrate   c) zinc sulfate
   d) magnesium nitrate   e) sodium sulfate   f) potassium chloride
20) Iron chloride can made by mixing iron hydroxide (an insoluble base) with hydrochloric acid. Describe the method you would use to produce pure, solid iron chloride in the lab.
21) How can you tell when a neutralisation reaction is complete if both the base and the salt are soluble in water?
22) Give a practical use of precipitation reactions.
23) What is electrolysis? Explain why only liquids can be electrolysed.
24) Draw a detailed diagram with half equations showing the electrolysis of sodium chloride.
25) Give one industrial use of sodium hydroxide and two uses of chlorine.
26) Why is cryolite used during the electrolysis of aluminium oxide?
27) Give two different uses of electroplating.

* Answers on page 108.

Velocity and Distance-Time Graphs

Ah, time for some lovely physics, you lucky thing. First off — <u>velocity</u>. The important thing to remember is that if something has <u>velocity</u> it has both <u>speed and direction</u>. Like you, <u>speeding towards success</u>...

Speed *and* Velocity are Both *How Fast* You're Going

<u>Speed and velocity</u> are both measured in <u>m/s</u> (or km/h or mph). They both simply say <u>how fast</u> you're going, but there's a <u>subtle difference</u> between them which <u>you need to know</u>:

> <u>Speed</u> is just <u>how fast</u> you're going (e.g. 30 mph or 20 m/s) with no regard to the direction.
> <u>Velocity</u> however must <u>also</u> have the <u>direction</u> specified, e.g. 30 mph north or 20 m/s, 060°.

Seems kinda fussy I know, but they expect you to remember that distinction, so there you go.

Distance-Time Graphs

These are a very nifty way of describing
something travelling through time and space:

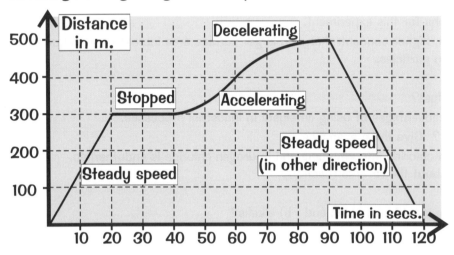

As you probably know,
<u>speed = distance ÷ time</u>.
So the <u>gradient</u> of a
distance-time graph tells
you <u>how fast</u> your object is
travelling. This is because
the gradient is the <u>change in
the distance</u> (vertical axis)
<u>divided by the change in time</u>
(horizontal axis). See — its
easy when you know how.

Very Important Notes:

1) <u>Gradient = speed</u>.
2) <u>Flat</u> sections are where it's <u>stationary</u> — it's <u>stopped</u>.
3) <u>Straight</u> uphill or downhill sections mean it is travelling at a <u>steady speed</u>.
4) The <u>steeper</u> the graph, the <u>faster</u> it's going.
5) <u>Downhill</u> sections mean it's <u>going back</u> toward its starting point.
6) <u>Curves</u> represent <u>acceleration</u> or <u>deceleration</u>.
7) A <u>steepening</u> curve means it's <u>speeding up</u> (increasing gradient).
8) A <u>levelling off</u> curve means it's <u>slowing down</u> (decreasing gradient).

Curves =
difficulty getting
out of chairs.

Calculating Speed *from a Distance-Time Graph* — It's Just the Gradient

For example the <u>speed</u> of the <u>return</u> section of the graph is:

$$\text{Speed} = \text{gradient} = \frac{\text{vertical}}{\text{horizontal}} = \frac{500}{30} = \underline{16.7 \text{ m/s}}$$

Don't forget that you have
to use the <u>scales</u> of the axes
to work out the gradient.
<u>Don't</u> measure in <u>cm</u>!

Ah, speed equals distance over time — that old chestnut...

Distance-time graphs have an annoying habit of popping up in exams <u>year after year</u> — so make sure you're
confident with <u>drawing</u> and <u>interpreting</u> them. Remember that the <u>gradient</u> of a distance-time graph is the <u>speed</u>
— so the <u>steeper</u> the line, the <u>faster</u> you're going. See — it's simple when you know how.

Acceleration and Velocity-Time Graphs

I bet you loved that distance-time graph, huh? Well here's its big brother — the <u>velocity-time</u> graph. Yikes.

Acceleration *is* How Quickly *Velocity is* Changing

Acceleration is <u>definitely not</u> the same as <u>velocity</u> or <u>speed</u>.
1) Acceleration is <u>how quickly</u> the velocity is <u>changing</u>.
2) This change in velocity can be a <u>CHANGE IN SPEED</u> or a <u>CHANGE IN DIRECTION</u> or <u>both</u>.
(You only have to worry about the change in speed bit for calculations.)

Acceleration — *The Formula:*

$$\text{Acceleration} = \frac{\text{Change in Velocity}}{\text{Time taken}}$$

Here 'v' is the <u>final velocity</u> and 'u' is the <u>initial velocity</u>.

Well, it's <u>just another formula</u>.
And it's got a <u>formula triangle</u> like all the others.
Mind you, there are <u>two tricky things</u> with this one. First there's the '(v – u)', which means working out the '<u>change in velocity</u>', as shown in the example below, rather than just putting a <u>simple value</u> for velocity or speed in. Secondly there's the <u>unit</u> of acceleration, which is <u>m/s²</u>.
<u>Not m/s</u>, which is <u>velocity</u>, but <u>m/s²</u>. Got it? No? Let's try once more: <u>Not m/s</u>, but <u>m/s²</u>.

Acceleration is the change in velocity (m/s) per second (s), = m/s².

<u>EXAMPLE:</u> A skulking cat accelerates from 2 m/s to 6 m/s in 5.6 s. Find its acceleration.
<u>ANSWER:</u> Using the formula triangle: a = (v – u) / t = (6 – 2) / 5.6
= 4 ÷ 5.6 = <u>0.71 m/s²</u>

Velocity-Time Graphs

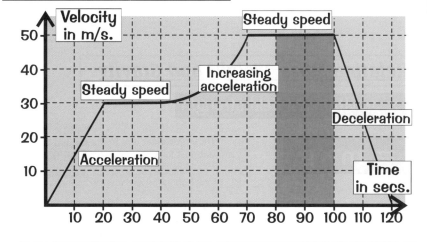

Very Important Notes:

1) <u>GRADIENT = ACCELERATION</u>.
2) <u>Flat sections</u> represent <u>steady speed</u>.
3) The <u>steeper</u> the graph, the <u>greater</u> the <u>acceleration</u> or <u>deceleration</u>.
4) <u>Uphill</u> sections (/) are <u>acceleration</u>.
5) <u>Downhill</u> sections (\\) are <u>deceleration</u>.
6) The <u>area</u> under any section of the graph (or all of it) is equal to the <u>distance travelled</u> in that <u>time interval</u>.
7) A <u>curve</u> means <u>changing acceleration</u>.

Calculating Acceleration, Velocity and Distance from a Velocity-Time Graph

1) The <u>acceleration</u> represented by the <u>first section</u> of the graph is:
$$\text{Acceleration} = \underline{\text{gradient}} = \frac{\text{vertical change}}{\text{horizontal change}} = \frac{30}{20} = \underline{1.5 \text{ m/s}^2}$$

2) The <u>velocity</u> at any point is simply found by <u>reading the value</u> off the <u>velocity axis</u>.

3) The <u>distance travelled</u> in any time interval is equal to the <u>area</u> under the graph. For example, the distance travelled between t = 80 s and t = 100 s is equal to the <u>shaded area</u>, which is equal to 20 × 50 = <u>1000 m</u>.

Understanding motion graphs — it can be a real uphill struggle...

Make sure you know all there is to know about velocity-time graphs — i.e. <u>learn those numbered points</u>.
You work out acceleration from the graph simply by applying the acceleration formula — change in velocity is the change on the vertical axis and time taken is the change on the horizontal axis.

Weight, Mass and Gravity

Now for something a bit more attractive — the force of gravity. Enjoy...

Gravitational Force is the Force of Attraction Between All Masses

Gravity attracts all masses, but you only notice it when one of the masses is really really big, e.g. a planet. Anything near a planet or star is attracted to it very strongly.

This has two important effects:

1) On the surface of a planet, it makes all things accelerate (see p.71) towards the ground (all with the same acceleration, g, which is about 10 m/s² on Earth).

2) It gives everything a weight.

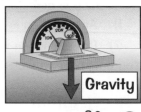

Weight and Mass are Not the Same

1) Mass is just the amount of 'stuff' in an object. For any given object this will have the same value anywhere in the universe.

2) Weight is caused by the pull of the gravitational force. In most questions the weight of an object is just the force of gravity pulling it towards the centre of the Earth.

3) An object has the same mass whether it's on Earth or on the Moon — but its weight will be different. A 1 kg mass will weigh less on the Moon (about 1.6 N) than it does on Earth (about 10 N), simply because the gravitational force pulling on it is less.

4) Weight is a force measured in newtons. It's measured using a spring balance or newton meter. Mass is not a force. It's measured in kilograms with a mass balance (an old-fashioned pair of balancing scales).

The Very Important Formula Relating Mass, Weight and Gravity

weight = mass × gravitational field strength

$$W = m \times g$$

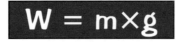

The acceleration due to gravity and the gravitational field strength are always the same value, no matter what planet or moon you're on.

1) Remember, weight and mass are not the same. Mass is in kg, weight is in newtons.

2) The letter "g" represents the strength of the gravity and its value is different for different planets. On Earth g ≈ 10 N/kg. On the Moon, where the gravity is weaker, g is only about 1.6 N/kg.

3) This formula is hideously easy to use:

Example: What is the weight, in newtons, of a 5 kg mass, both on Earth and on the Moon?
Answer: "W = m × g". On Earth: W = 5 × 10 = 50 N (The weight of the 5 kg mass is 50 N.)
On the Moon: W = 5 × 1.6 = 8 N (The weight of the 5 kg mass is 8 N.)

See what I mean. Hideously easy — as long as you've learnt what all the letters mean.

I don't think you understand the gravity of this situation...

The difference between weight and mass can be tricky to get your head around, but it's well important. Weight is the force of gravity acting on a mass, and mass is the amount of stuff, measured in kg. Now might be a good time to get that equation memorised as well — that's right — cover, scribble and check.

Resultant Forces

Gravity isn't the only force in town — there are other forces such as <u>driving forces</u> or <u>air resistance</u>. What you need to be able to work out is how all these forces <u>add up together</u>.

Resultant Force *is the Overall Force* on a Point or Object

The notion of <u>resultant force</u> is a really important one for you to get your head round:

1) In most <u>real</u> situations there are at least <u>two forces</u> acting on an object along any direction.

2) The <u>overall</u> effect of these forces will decide the <u>motion</u> of the object — whether it will <u>accelerate</u>, <u>decelerate</u> or stay at a <u>steady speed</u>.

3) If you have a <u>number of forces</u> acting at a single point, you can replace them with a <u>single force</u> (so long as the single force has the <u>same effect on the motion</u> as the original forces acting all together).

4) If the forces all act along the same line (they're all parallel and act in the same or the opposite direction), the <u>overall effect</u> is found by just <u>adding or subtracting</u> them.

5) The overall force you get is called the <u>resultant force</u>.

Example: Stationary Teapot — *All Forces Balance*

1) The force of <u>GRAVITY</u> (or weight) is acting <u>downwards</u>.

2) This causes a <u>REACTION FORCE</u> (see p.75) from the surface <u>pushing up</u> on the object.

3) This is the <u>only way</u> it can be in <u>BALANCE</u>.

4) <u>Without</u> a reaction force, it would <u>accelerate</u> <u>downwards</u> due to the pull of gravity.

5) The <u>resultant</u> force on the teapot is zero: 10 N − 10 N = 0 N.

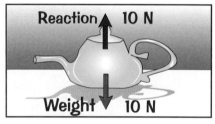

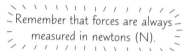
Remember that forces are always measured in newtons (N).

A Resultant Force *Means a* Change in Velocity

1) If there is a resultant force acting on an object, then the object will <u>change its state of rest or motion</u>.

2) In other words it causes a <u>change in the object's velocity</u>.

You Should be Able to *Find the Resultant Force* Acting in a Straight Line

EXAMPLE: Benny is cruising along to Las Vegas in his vintage sports car. He applies a driving force of <u>1000 N</u>, but has to overcome air resistance of <u>600 N</u>. What is the <u>resultant force</u>? Will the car's velocity <u>change</u>?

Driving Force: 1000 N
Air Resistance: 600 N

Resultant Force: 400 N

ANSWER: Say that the forces pointing to the <u>left</u> are pointing in the <u>positive direction</u>. The resultant force = 1000 N − 600 N = <u>400 N to the left</u>. If there is a resultant force then there is always an acceleration, so Benny's velocity <u>will</u> change. Viva Las Vegas.

And you're moving forward — what a result...

Resultant forces are just about <u>adding</u> and <u>subtracting</u> really — the trick is to make sure you've <u>accounted for</u> <u>everything</u>. Next up, some of the <u>thrilling physics</u> you can understand once you have resultant forces figured out.

Forces and Acceleration

Around about the time of the Great Plague in the 1660s, a chap called <u>Isaac Newton</u> worked out his <u>Laws of Motion</u>. At first they might seem kind of obscure or irrelevant, but to be perfectly blunt, if you can't understand this page then you'll never understand <u>forces and motion</u>.

An Object Needs a Force to Start Moving

> If the resultant force on a <u>stationary</u> object is <u>zero</u>, the object will <u>remain stationary</u>.

Things <u>don't just start moving</u> on their own, there has to be a <u>resultant force</u> (see p.73) to get them started.

No Resultant Force Means No Change in Velocity

> If there is <u>no resultant force</u> on a <u>moving</u> object it'll just carry on moving at the <u>same velocity</u>.

1) When a train or car or bus or anything else is <u>moving</u> at a <u>constant velocity</u> then the <u>forces</u> on it must all be <u>balanced</u>.

2) Never let yourself entertain the <u>ridiculous idea</u> that things need a constant overall force to <u>keep</u> them moving — NO NO NO NO NO NO!

3) To keep going at a <u>steady speed</u>, there must be <u>zero resultant force</u> — and don't you forget it.

A Resultant Force Means Acceleration

> If there is a <u>non-zero resultant force</u>, then the object will <u>accelerate</u> in the direction of the force.

1) A non-zero <u>resultant</u> force will always produce <u>acceleration</u> (or deceleration).

2) This "<u>acceleration</u>" can take <u>five</u> different forms: <u>Starting</u>, <u>stopping</u>, <u>speeding up</u>, <u>slowing down</u> and <u>changing direction</u>.

3) On a force diagram, the <u>arrows</u> will be <u>unequal</u>:

<u>Don't ever say</u>: "If something's moving there must be an overall resultant force acting on it".
Not so. If there's an <u>overall</u> force it will always <u>accelerate</u>.
You get <u>steady</u> speed when there is <u>zero</u> resultant force.
I wonder how many times I need to say that same thing before you remember it?

Steady Speed Bus Tours Ltd. — providing consistent service since 1926...

<u>Objects in space</u> don't need a driving force to keep travelling at a steady speed — it's only because of <u>air resistance</u> and <u>friction</u> that we do. A steady speed means that there is <u>zero resultant force</u>.

Forces and Acceleration

More fun stuff on forces and acceleration here. The big equation to learn is $F = ma$ — it's a really important one and you <u>will</u> be tested on it. Remember that the F is always the <u>resultant force</u> — that's important too.

A Non-Zero Resultant Force Produces an Acceleration

Any <u>resultant force</u> will produce <u>acceleration</u>, and this is the <u>formula</u> for it:

$$F = ma \quad \text{or} \quad a = F/m$$

m = mass in kilograms (kg)
a = acceleration in metres per second squared (m/s²)
F is the <u>resultant force</u> in newtons (N)

<u>EXAMPLE:</u> A car of mass of 1750 kg has an engine which provides a driving force of 5200 N.
At 70 mph the drag force acting on the car is 5150 N.
Find its acceleration a) when first setting off from rest b) at 70 mph.

<u>ANSWER:</u> 1) First draw a force diagram for both cases (no need to show the vertical forces):

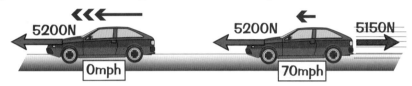

2) Work out the resultant force and acceleration of the car in each case.

Resultant force = 5200 N
a = F/m = 5200 ÷ 1750 = <u>3.0 m/s²</u>

Resultant force = 5200 – 5150 = 50 N
a = F/m = 50 ÷ 1750 = <u>0.03 m/s²</u>

Reaction Forces are Equal and Opposite

> When <u>two objects interact</u>, the forces they exert on each other are <u>equal and opposite</u>.

1) That means if you <u>push</u> something, say a shopping trolley, the trolley will <u>push back</u> against you, <u>just as hard</u>.

2) And as soon as you <u>stop</u> pushing, <u>so does the trolley</u>. Kinda clever really.

3) So far so good. The slightly tricky thing to get your head round is this — if the forces are always equal, <u>how does anything ever go anywhere</u>? The important thing to remember is that the two forces are acting on <u>different objects</u>. Think about a pair of ice skaters:

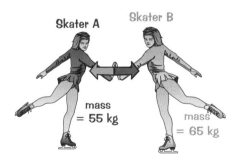

When skater A pushes on skater B (the '<u>action</u>' force), she feels an equal and opposite force from skater B's hand (the '<u>reaction</u>' force). Both skaters feel the <u>same sized force</u>, in <u>opposite directions</u>, and so accelerate away from each other.

Skater A will be <u>accelerated</u> more than skater B, though, because she has a smaller mass — remember $a = F/m$.

4) It's the same sort of thing when you go <u>swimming</u>. You <u>push</u> back against the <u>water</u> with your arms and legs, and the water pushes you forwards with an <u>equal-sized force</u> in the <u>opposite direction</u>.

I have a reaction to forces — they bring me out in a rash...

This is the real deal. Like... proper Physics. It was <u>pretty fantastic</u> at the time it was discovered — suddenly people understood how forces and motion worked, they could work out the <u>orbits of planets</u> and everything. Inspired? No? Shame. Learn it anyway — you're really going to struggle in the exam if you don't.

Frictional Force and Terminal Velocity

Ever wondered why it's so hard to run into a hurricane whilst wearing a sandwich board? Read on to find out...

Friction is Always There to Slow Things Down

1) If an object has <u>no force</u> propelling it along it will always <u>slow down and stop</u> because of <u>friction</u> (unless you're in space where there's nothing to rub against).
2) Friction always acts in the <u>opposite</u> direction to movement.
3) To travel at a <u>steady</u> speed, the driving force needs to <u>balance</u> the frictional forces.
4) You get friction between <u>two surfaces</u> in contact, or when an object passes <u>through a fluid</u> (<u>drag</u>).

RESISTANCE OR "DRAG" FROM FLUIDS (air or liquid)

Most of the resistive forces are caused by <u>air resistance</u> or "<u>drag</u>". The most important factor <u>by far</u> in <u>reducing drag</u> in fluids is keeping the shape of the object <u>streamlined</u>.
The <u>opposite</u> extreme is a <u>parachute</u> which is about as <u>high drag</u> as you can get — which is, of course, <u>the whole idea</u>.

Drag Increases as the Speed Increases

<u>Frictional forces</u> from fluids always <u>increase with speed</u>.
A car has <u>much more</u> friction to <u>work against</u> when travelling at <u>70 mph</u> compared to <u>30 mph</u>. So at 70 mph the engine has to work <u>much harder</u> just to maintain a <u>steady speed</u>.

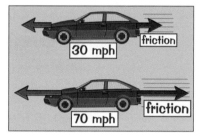

Objects Falling Through Fluids Reach a Terminal Velocity

When falling objects first <u>set off</u>, the force of gravity is <u>much more</u> than the <u>frictional force</u> slowing them down, so they accelerate. As the <u>speed increases</u> the friction <u>builds up</u>. This gradually <u>reduces</u> the <u>acceleration</u> until eventually the <u>frictional force</u> is <u>equal</u> to the <u>accelerating force</u> and then it won't accelerate any more. It will have reached its maximum speed or <u>terminal velocity</u> and will fall at a steady speed.

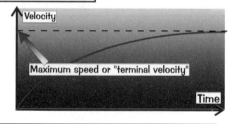

The Terminal Velocity of Falling Objects Depends on their Shape and Area

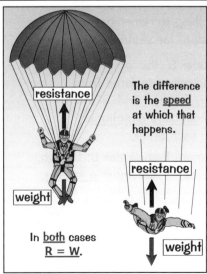

The difference is the <u>speed</u> at which that happens.
In <u>both</u> cases R = W.

The <u>accelerating force</u> acting on <u>all</u> falling objects is <u>gravity</u> and it would make them all fall at the <u>same</u> rate, if it wasn't for <u>air resistance</u>. This means that on the Moon, where there's <u>no air</u>, hamsters and feathers dropped simultaneously will hit the ground <u>together</u>. However, on Earth, <u>air resistance</u> causes things to fall at <u>different</u> speeds, and the <u>terminal velocity</u> of any object is determined by its <u>drag</u> in <u>comparison</u> to its <u>weight</u>.
The frictional force depends on its <u>shape and area</u>.

The most important example is the human <u>skydiver</u>. Without his parachute open he has quite a <u>small</u> area and a force of "<u>W = mg</u>" pulling him down. He reaches a <u>terminal velocity</u> of about <u>120 mph</u>. But with the parachute <u>open</u>, there's much more <u>air resistance</u> (at any given speed) and still only the same force "<u>W = mg</u>" pulling him down. This means his <u>terminal velocity</u> comes right down to about <u>15 mph</u>, which is a <u>safe speed</u> to hit the ground at.

Learning about air resistance — it can be a real drag...

There are a few really important things on this page. 1) When you fall through a fluid, there's a frictional force (drag), 2) frictional force increases with speed, so 3) you eventually reach terminal velocity.

Stopping Distances

And now a page on stopping distances. This may seem a bit out of kilter with the rest of the section, but it's a <u>real world application</u> of the physics of forces. See, I told you it was useful... and fun... right?

Many Factors **Affect Your Total** Stopping Distance

1) Looking at things simply — if you <u>need to stop</u> in a <u>given distance</u>, then the <u>faster</u> a vehicle's going, the <u>bigger braking force</u> it'll need.

2) Likewise, for any given braking force, the <u>faster</u> you're going, the <u>greater your stopping distance</u>. But in real life it's not quite that simple — if your maximum braking force isn't enough, you'll go further before you stop.

3) The total <u>stopping distance</u> of a vehicle is the distance covered in the time between the driver <u>first spotting</u> a hazard and the vehicle coming to a <u>complete stop</u>.

4) The <u>stopping distance</u> is <u>the sum</u> of the <u>thinking distance</u> and the <u>braking distance</u>.

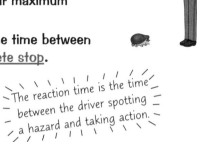

~The reaction time is the time between the driver spotting a hazard and taking action.~

1) Thinking Distance

"The distance the vehicle travels during the driver's reaction time".

It's affected by <u>two main factors</u>:

a) How fast you're going — Obviously. Whatever your reaction time, the <u>faster</u> you're going, the <u>further</u> you'll go.

b) How dopey you are — This is affected by <u>tiredness</u>, <u>drugs</u>, <u>alcohol</u> and a <u>careless</u> blasé attitude.

<u>Bad visibility</u> and <u>distractions</u> can also be a major factor in accidents — lashing rain, messing about with the radio, bright oncoming lights, etc. might mean that a driver <u>doesn't notice</u> a hazard until they're quite close to it. It <u>doesn't</u> affect your thinking distance, but you <u>start thinking</u> about stopping <u>nearer</u> to the hazard, and so you're <u>more likely</u> to crash.

The figures below for typical stopping distances are from the Highway Code. It's frightening to see just how far it takes to stop when you're going at 70 mph.

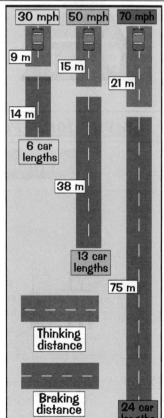

30 mph	50 mph	70 mph
9 m	15 m	21 m
14 m	38 m	75 m
6 car lengths	13 car lengths	24 car lengths

Thinking distance

Braking distance

2) Braking Distance

"The distance the car travels under the breaking force".

It's affected by <u>four main factors</u>:

a) How fast you're going — The <u>faster</u> you're going, the <u>further</u> it takes to stop.

b) How good your brakes are — All brakes must be checked and maintained <u>regularly</u>. Worn or faulty brakes will let you down <u>catastrophically</u> just when you need them the <u>most</u>, i.e. in an <u>emergency</u>.

c) How good the tyres are — Tyres should have a minimum <u>tread depth</u> of <u>1.6 mm</u> in order to be able to get rid of the <u>water</u> in wet conditions. Leaves, diesel spills and muck on the road can <u>greatly increase</u> the braking distance, and cause the car to <u>skid</u> too.

d) How good the grip is — This depends on <u>three things</u>: 1) <u>road surface</u>, 2) <u>weather</u> conditions, 3) <u>tyres</u>.

<u>Wet</u> or <u>icy roads</u> are always much more <u>slippy</u> than dry roads, but often you only discover this when you try to <u>brake</u> hard. You don't have as much grip, so you travel further before stopping.

Stop right there — and learn this page...

Without <u>tread</u>, a tyre will simply <u>ride</u> on a <u>layer of water</u> and skid <u>very easily</u>. This is called "<u>aquaplaning</u>" and isn't nearly as cool as it sounds. <u>Snow and ice</u> are also very hazardous because it is difficult for the tyres to <u>get a grip</u>.

Work and Potential Energy

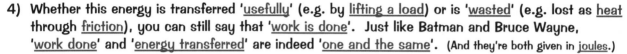

**When a _force_ moves an _object_ through a _distance_,
ENERGY IS TRANSFERRED and WORK IS DONE.**

That statement sounds far more complicated than it needs to. Try this:

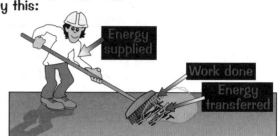

1) Whenever something _moves_, something else is providing some sort of '_effort_' to move it.
2) The thing putting the _effort_ in needs a _supply_ of energy (like _fuel_ or _food_ or _electricity_ etc.).
3) It then does '_work_' by _moving_ the object — and one way or another it _transfers_ the energy it receives (as fuel) into _other forms_.
4) Whether this energy is transferred '_usefully_' (e.g. by _lifting a load_) or is '_wasted_' (e.g. lost as _heat_ through _friction_), you can still say that '_work is done_'. Just like Batman and Bruce Wayne, '_work done_' and '_energy transferred_' are indeed '_one and the same_'. (And they're both given in _joules_.)

It's Just Another Trivial Formula:

Work Done = Force × Distance

Whether the force is _friction_ or _weight_ or _tension in a rope_, it's always the same. To find how much _energy_ has been _transferred_ (in joules), you just multiply the force in N by the _distance moved in m_. Easy as that. I'll show you...

<u>EXAMPLE:</u> Some hooligan kids drag an old tractor tyre <u>5 m</u> over rough ground. They pull with a total force of <u>340 N</u>. Find the energy transferred.
<u>ANSWER:</u> W = F×d = 340 × 5 = <u>1700 J</u>. Phew — easy peasy isn't it?

Gravitational Potential Energy **is Energy** Due to Height

Gravitational Potential Energy = mass × g × height

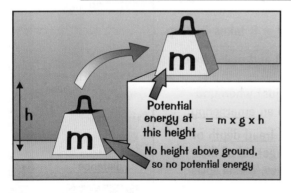

Potential energy at this height = m x g x h

No height above ground, so no potential energy

Gravitational potential energy (measured in joules) is the energy that an object has by virtue of (because of) its _vertical position_ in a _gravitational field_. When an object is raised vertically, _work is done_ against the _force of gravity_ (it takes effort to lift it up) and the object gains gravitational potential energy. On _Earth_ the gravitational field strength (g) is approximately <u>10 N/kg</u>.

<u>EXAMPLE:</u> A sheep of mass 47 kg is slowly raised through 6.3 m. Find the gain in potential energy.
<u>ANSWER:</u> Just plug the numbers into the formula:
E_p = mgh = 47 × 10 × 6.3 = <u>2961 J</u>
(Joules because it's _energy_.)

What do you call a sheep with no eyes and no legs? — Dunno? — A Cloud!

Revise work done — what else...

Remember "_energy transferred_" and "_work done_" are the same thing. By lifting something up you do work by transferring _chemical energy_ to _gravitational potential energy_. Think about that next time you're bench-pressing sheep.

Kinetic Energy

Kinetic Energy is Energy of Movement

Anything that's moving has kinetic energy.
There's a slightly tricky formula for it, so you have to concentrate a little bit harder for this one.
But hey, that's life — it can be real tough sometimes:

$$\text{Kinetic Energy} = \tfrac{1}{2} \times \text{mass} \times \text{speed}^2$$

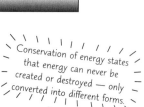

EXAMPLE: A car of mass 2450 kg is travelling at 38 m/s.
Calculate its kinetic energy.
ANSWER: It's pretty easy. You just plug the numbers into the formula — but watch the 'v²'!
K.E. = $\tfrac{1}{2}mv^2$ = $\tfrac{1}{2} \times 2450 \times 38^2$ = __1 768 900 J__ (Joules because it's energy.)

Remember, the kinetic energy of something depends both on mass and speed.
The more it weighs and the faster it's going, the bigger its kinetic energy will be.

small mass, not fast
low kinetic energy

big fast
lorries Ltd

big mass, real fast
high kinetic energy

Kinetic Energy Transferred is Work Done

Conservation of energy states that energy can never be created or destroyed — only converted into different forms.

When a Car is Moving It Has Kinetic Energy

1) A moving car can have a lot of kinetic energy. To slow a car down this kinetic energy needs to be converted into other types of energy (using the law of conservation of energy).

2) To stop a car, the kinetic energy ($\tfrac{1}{2}mv^2$) has to be converted to heat energy as friction between the wheels and the brake pads, causing the temperature of the brakes to increase:

$$\text{Kinetic Energy Transferred} = \text{Work Done by Brakes}$$
$$\tfrac{1}{2}mv^2 = F \times d$$

m = mass of car and passengers (in kg) v = speed of car (in m/s) F = maximum braking force (in N) d = braking distance (in m).

Falling Objects Convert Ep into Ek...

When something falls, its potential energy (see p.78) is converted into kinetic energy. So the further it falls, the faster it goes.

$$\text{Kinetic energy gained} = \text{Potential Energy lost}$$

P.E.
↓
K.E.

...and some of this Ek is Transferred into Heat and Sound

When meteors and space shuttles enter the atmosphere, they have a very high kinetic energy. Friction due to collisions with particles in the atmosphere transfers some of their kinetic energy to heat energy and work is done. The temperatures can become so extreme that most meteors burn up completely and never hit the Earth. Only the biggest meteors make it through to the Earth's surface — these are called meteorites.

Space shuttles have heat shields made from special materials which lose heat quickly, allowing the shuttle to re-enter the atmosphere without burning up.

Kinetic energy — just get a move on and learn it, OK...

So that's why I've not been hit by a meteor — most get burned up. Now you know. What you probably don't know yet, though, is that rather lovely formula at the top of the page. I mean, gosh, it's got more than three letters in it...

Forces and Elasticity

Forces aren't just important for cars and falling sheep — you can stretch things with them as well. It can sound quite tricky at first, but it's not as hard as it looks. And there is only one equation to memorise — hurrah.

Work Done to an Elastic Object is Stored as Elastic Potential Energy

1) When you apply a force to an object you may cause it to stretch and change in shape.

2) Any object that can go back to its original shape after the force has been removed is an elastic object.

3) Work is done to an elastic object to change its shape. This energy is not lost but is stored by the object as elastic potential energy.

4) The elastic potential energy is then converted to kinetic energy when the force is removed and the object returns to its original shape, e.g. when a spring or an elastic band bounces back.

Elastic potential energy — useful for passing exams and scaring small children

Extension of an Elastic Object is Directly Proportional to Force...

If a spring is supported at the top and then a weight attached to the bottom, it stretches.

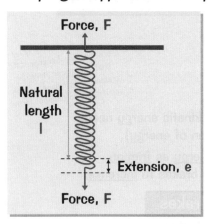
Force, F
Natural length
l
Extension, e
Force, F

1) The extension, e, of a stretched spring (or other elastic object) is directly proportional to the load or force applied, F. The extension is measured in metres, and the force is measured in newtons.

2) This is the equation you need to learn:

$$F = k \times e$$

3) k is the spring constant. Its value depends on the material that you are stretching and it's measured in newtons per metre (N/m).

...but this Stops Working when the Force is Great Enough

There's a limit to the amount of force you can apply to an object for the extension to keep on increasing proportionally.

1) The graph shows force against extension for an elastic object.

2) For small forces, force and extension are proportional. So the first part of the graph shows a straight-line relationship between force and extension.

3) There is a maximum force that the elastic object can take and still extend proportionally. This is known as the limit of proportionality and is shown on the graph at the point marked P.

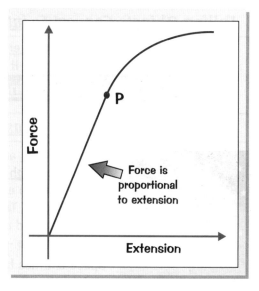
Force is proportional to extension
Force
Extension

I could make a joke, but I don't want to stretch myself...

Scaring small children aside, elastic potential is really quite a useful form of energy. Think of all the things we rely on that use it — catapults, trampolines, scrunchies... Ah, elastic potential energy — thank you for enriching our lives.

Power

Power is a concept that pops up in both <u>forces</u> and <u>electricity</u>. This is because, at its most fundamental level, power is just about the rate of <u>energy transferred</u> — and energy is transferred wherever you look.

Power *is the "Rate of Doing Work" — i.e. How Much per Second*

<u>Power</u> is <u>not</u> the same thing as <u>force</u>, nor <u>energy</u>. A <u>powerful</u> machine is not necessarily one which can exert a strong <u>force</u> (though it usually ends up that way).
A <u>powerful</u> machine is one which transfers <u>a lot of energy in a short space of time</u>.
This is the <u>very easy formula</u> for power:

$$Power = \frac{Work\ done\ (or\ energy\ transferred)}{Time\ taken}$$

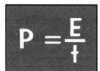 $P = \frac{E}{t}$

 $\frac{E}{P \times t}$

Power *is Measured in Watts (or J/s)*

The proper unit of power is the <u>watt</u>. <u>One watt = 1 joule of energy transferred per second.</u>
<u>Power</u> means "how much energy <u>per second</u>", so <u>watts</u> are the same as "<u>joules per second</u>" (J/s).
Don't ever say "watts per second" — it's <u>nonsense</u>.

<u>Example:</u> A motor transfers 4.8 kJ of useful energy in 2 minutes. Find its power output.
<u>Answer:</u> P = E / t = 4800/120 = 40 W (or 40 J/s)
(Note that the kJ had to be turned into J, and the minutes into seconds.)

4.8 kJ of useful energy in **2 minutes**

Calculating Your Power Output

There are a few different ways to measure the power output of a <u>person</u>:

a) *The Timed Run Upstairs:*

In this case the "<u>energy transferred</u>" is the <u>potential energy you gain</u> (= mgh).
Hence <u>Power = mgh/t</u>

<u>Power output</u>
= En. transferred/time
= mgh/t
= (62×10×12)÷14
= <u>531 W</u>

b) *The Timed Acceleration:*

This time the <u>energy transferred</u> is the <u>kinetic energy you gain</u> (= ½mv²).
Hence <u>Power = ½mv²/t</u>

<u>Power output</u>
= En. transferred/time
= ½mv²/t
= (½×62×8²)÷4
= <u>496 W</u>

To get <u>accurate results</u> from these experiments, you have to do them several times and find an <u>average</u>.

Power — you need to know watt's watt...

Power is the amount of energy transferred per second, and it's measured in <u>watts</u>. The watt is named after James Watt, a Scottish inventor and engineer who did a lot of work on steam engines in the 1700s. Nice. Make sure you <u>learn the formula</u> and power questions should be a doddle.

Momentum and Collisions

A <u>large</u> rhino running very <u>fast</u> at you is going to be a lot harder to stop than a scrawny one out for a Sunday afternoon stroll — that's momentum for you.

Momentum = Mass × Velocity

1) Momentum (p) is a <u>property</u> of <u>moving objects</u>.

2) The <u>greater</u> the <u>mass</u> of an object and the <u>greater</u> its <u>velocity</u> (see p.70) the <u>more momentum</u> the object has.

3) Momentum is a <u>vector</u> quantity — it has size <u>and</u> direction (like <u>velocity</u>, but not speed).

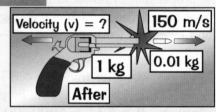

Momentum (kg m/s) = Mass (kg) × Velocity (m/s)

Momentum Before = Momentum After

In a <u>closed system</u>, the total momentum <u>before</u> an event (e.g. a collision) is the same as <u>after</u> the event. This is called <u>Conservation of Momentum</u>.

A <u>closed system</u> is just a fancy way of saying that no external forces act.

Example 1: Collisions

Two skaters approach each other, collide and move off together as shown. At what velocity do they move after the collision?

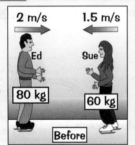

2 m/s   1.5 m/s
Ed   Sue
80 kg   60 kg
Before

Velocity (v) =
(80+60) kg
After

1) Choose which direction is <u>positive</u>.

   I'll say "<u>positive</u>" means "<u>to the right</u>".

2) <u>Total momentum before</u> collision
   = momentum of Ed + momentum of Sue
   = {80 × 2} + {60 × (–1.5)}
   = <u>70 kg m/s</u>

3) <u>Total momentum after</u> collision
   = momentum of Ed and Sue together
   = <u>140 × v</u>

4) So 140v = 70, i.e. <u>v = 0.5 m/s to the right</u>

Example 2: Explosions

A gun fires a bullet as shown. At what speed does the gun move backwards?

Velocity (v) = ?   150 m/s
1 kg   0.01 kg
After

1) Choose which direction is <u>positive</u>.
   Again, I reckon "<u>positive</u>" means "<u>to the right</u>".

2) <u>Total momentum before</u> firing = <u>0 kg m/s</u>

3) <u>Total momentum after</u> firing
   = momentum of bullet + momentum of gun
   = (0.01 × 150) + (1 × v)
   = <u>1.5 + v</u>

   This is the gun's recoil.

   The momentum of a system <u>before</u> an explosion is <u>zero</u>, so, due to <u>conservation of momentum</u>, the total momentum after an explosion is <u>zero too</u>.

4) So 1.5 + v = 0, i.e. v = –1.5 m/s
   So the gun moves <u>backwards</u> at <u>1.5 m/s</u>.

Forces Cause Changes in Momentum

1) When a <u>force</u> acts on an object, it causes a <u>change</u> in momentum.

2) A <u>larger</u> force means a <u>faster</u> change of momentum (and so a greater <u>acceleration</u>).

3) Likewise, if someone's momentum changes <u>very quickly</u> (like in a <u>car crash</u>), the <u>forces</u> on the body will be very <u>large</u>, and more likely to cause <u>injury</u>.

4) This is why cars are designed with safety features that slow people down over a <u>longer time</u> when they have a crash — the longer it takes for a change in <u>momentum</u>, the <u>smaller</u> the <u>force</u>.

Learn this stuff — it'll only take a moment... um...

Momentum's a pretty fundamental bit of Physics — so make sure you learn it properly. Right then, momentum is always <u>conserved</u> in collisions and explosions when there are no external forces acting. Job's a good 'un.

Car Design and Safety

A lot of the physics you've seen over the last few pages can be applied in the real world to designing <u>safe and efficient</u> cars. It's all about forces, energy, acceleration and momentum. <u>Sweet as a nut</u>.

Brakes do Work Against the Kinetic Energy of the Car

When you <u>apply the brakes</u> to slow down a car, <u>work is done</u> (see p.78).
The brakes reduce the <u>kinetic energy</u> of the car by transferring it into <u>heat</u> (and sound) energy (see p.79).
In <u>traditional</u> braking systems that would be the <u>end of the story</u>, but new <u>regenerative braking systems</u> used in some <u>electric</u> or <u>hybrid</u> cars <u>make use</u> of the energy, instead of converting it all into heat during braking.

1) <u>Regenerative brakes</u> use the <u>system</u> that <u>drives</u> the vehicle to do the <u>majority of the braking</u>.

2) Rather than converting the kinetic energy of the vehicle into heat energy, the brakes put the vehicle's <u>motor into reverse</u>. With the motor running <u>backwards</u>, the wheels are <u>slowed</u>.

3) At the same time, the motor acts as an <u>electric generator</u>, converting kinetic energy into <u>electrical energy</u> that is stored as <u>chemical energy</u> in the vehicle's <u>battery</u>. This is the advantage of regenerative brakes — they <u>store</u> the energy of braking rather than <u>wasting</u> it. It's a nifty chain of energy transfer.

Cars are Designed to Convert Kinetic Energy Safely in a Crash

1) If a car crashes it will <u>slow down very quickly</u> — this means that a lot of <u>kinetic energy</u> is converted into other forms of energy in a <u>short amount of time</u>, which can be dangerous for the <u>people</u> inside.

2) In a crash, there'll be a <u>big change in momentum</u> (see p.82) over a <u>very short time</u>, so the people inside the car experience <u>huge forces</u> that could be fatal.

3) Cars are <u>designed</u> to convert the <u>kinetic energy</u> of the car and its passengers in a way that is <u>safest</u> for the car's occupants. They often do this by <u>increasing the time</u> over which momentum changes happen, which <u>lessens</u> the forces on the passengers.

airbag

seat belt

<u>CRUMPLE ZONES</u> at the front and back of the car crumple up <u>on impact</u>.

- The car's kinetic energy is converted into other forms of energy by the car body as it <u>changes shape</u>.
- Crumple zones <u>increase the impact time</u>, decreasing the force produced by the change in momentum.

<u>SIDE IMPACT BARS</u> are strong metal tubes fitted into car door panels. They help direct the kinetic energy of the crash <u>away from the passengers</u> to other areas of the car, such as the crumple zones.

<u>SEAT BELTS</u> stretch slightly, <u>increasing the time</u> taken for the wearer to stop. This <u>reduces the forces</u> acting in the chest. Some of the kinetic energy of the wearer is <u>absorbed</u> by the seat belt <u>stretching</u>.

<u>AIR BAGS</u> also slow you down more <u>gradually</u> and prevent you from <u>hitting hard surfaces</u> inside the car.

Cars Have Different Power Ratings

1) The <u>size</u> and <u>design</u> of car engines determine how <u>powerful</u> they are.

2) The <u>more powerful</u> an engine is, the more <u>energy</u> it transfers from its <u>fuel</u> every second, and so the <u>faster</u> its top speed can be.

3) E.g. the <u>power output</u> of a typical small car will be around 50 kW and a sports car will be about 100 kW (some are <u>much</u> higher).

Sports car power = 100 kW

Small car power = 50 kW

4) Cars are also designed to be <u>aerodynamic</u>. This means that they are shaped in such a way that <u>air flows</u> very easily and smoothly past them, so minimising their <u>air resistance</u>.

5) Cars reach their <u>top speed</u> when the resistive force <u>equals</u> the driving force provided by the engine (see p.76). So, with <u>less air resistance</u> to overcome, the car can reach a <u>higher speed</u> before this happens. Aerodynamic cars therefore have <u>higher top speeds</u>.

Don't let all this revising drive you crazy...

Driving can be quite <u>risky</u> when you look at the physics of it — which is why so much time and effort is put into making cars as safe as possible. There's a lot of info on this page but sadly you've got to learn it. Sozzles.

Static Electricity

Static electricity is all about charges which are <u>not</u> free to move, e.g. in insulating materials. This causes them to build up in one place and it often ends with a <u>spark</u> or a <u>shock</u> when they do finally move.

Build-up of Static is Caused by Friction

1) When certain <u>insulating</u> materials are <u>rubbed</u> together, negatively charged electrons will be <u>scraped off one</u> and <u>dumped</u> on the other.

2) This'll leave a <u>positive</u> static charge on one and a <u>negative</u> static charge on the other.

3) <u>Which way</u> the electrons are transferred <u>depends</u> on the <u>two materials</u> involved.

4) Electrically charged objects <u>attract</u> small objects placed near them.
(Try this: rub a balloon on a woolly pully — then put it near tiddly bits of paper and watch them jump.)

5) The classic examples are <u>polythene</u> and <u>acetate</u> rods being rubbed with a <u>cloth duster</u>, as shown in the diagrams.

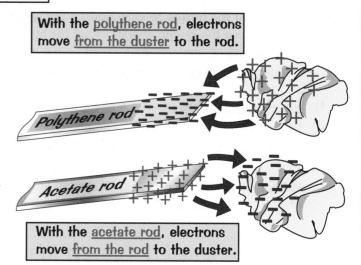

With the <u>polythene rod</u>, electrons move <u>from the duster</u> to the rod.

With the <u>acetate rod</u>, electrons move <u>from the rod</u> to the duster.

Only Electrons Move — Never the Positive Charges

<u>Watch out for this in exams.</u> Both +ve and −ve electrostatic charges are only ever produced by the movement of <u>electrons</u>. The positive charges <u>definitely do not move</u>!

A positive static charge is always caused by electrons <u>moving</u> away elsewhere. The material that <u>loses</u> the electrons loses some negative charge, and is <u>left with an equal positive charge</u>, as shown above. Don't forget!

Like Charges Repel, Opposite Charges Attract

This is <u>easy</u> and, I'd have thought, <u>kind of obvious</u>. When two electrically charged objects are brought close together they <u>exert a force</u> on one another.

Two things with <u>opposite</u> electric charges are <u>attracted</u> to each other. Two things with the <u>same</u> electric charge will <u>repel</u> each other. These forces get <u>weaker</u> the <u>further apart</u> the two things are.

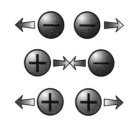

Charges can Move Easily Through Conductors

1) Electrical charges can <u>move easily</u> through some materials. These materials are called <u>conductors</u>.

2) <u>Metals</u> are known to be <u>good</u> conductors.

Stay away from electrons — they're a negative influence...

The bog standard electrical charge carrier is the <u>electron</u>. Those <u>little devils</u> get just about everywhere in metals, taking <u>charge</u> pretty much wherever you want it. But in insulators they're <u>stuck</u> and can't move easily — its only when they're <u>manually scraped off</u> that they ever get to go anywhere, poor blighters...

Current and Potential Difference

Isn't <u>electricity</u> great. Mind you it's pretty bad news if the <u>words</u> don't mean anything to you...
Hey, I know — learn them now!

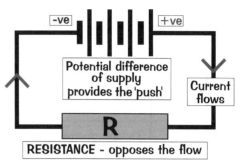

1) <u>Current</u> is the <u>flow</u> of electric charge round the circuit. Current will <u>only flow</u> through a component if there is a <u>potential difference</u> across that component. Unit: ampere, A.

2) <u>Potential Difference</u> is the <u>driving force</u> that pushes the current round. Unit: volt, V.

3) <u>Resistance</u> is anything in the circuit which <u>slows the flow down</u>. Unit: ohm, Ω.

> The <u>greater the resistance</u> across a component,
> the <u>smaller the current</u> that flows
> (for a given potential difference across the component).

Total Charge Through a Circuit Depends on Current and Time

1) <u>Current</u> is the <u>rate of flow</u> of <u>charge</u>. When <u>current</u> (I) flows past a point in a circuit for a length of <u>time</u> (t) then the <u>charge</u> (Q) that has passed is given by this formula:

2) <u>Current</u> is measured in <u>amperes</u> (A), <u>charge</u> is measured in <u>coulombs</u> (C), <u>time</u> is measured in <u>seconds</u> (s).

$$\text{Current} = \frac{\text{Charge}}{\text{Time}} \qquad I = \frac{Q}{t}$$

3) <u>More charge</u> passes around the circuit when a <u>bigger current</u> flows.

> <u>EXAMPLE:</u> A battery charger passes a current of 2.5 A through a cell over a period of 4 hours. How much charge does the charger transfer to the cell altogether?
>
> <u>ANSWER:</u> $Q = I \times t = 2.5 \times (4 \times 60 \times 60) = 36\,000$ C (36 kC).

Potential Difference (P. D.) is the Work Done Per Unit Charge

1) The potential difference (or <u>voltage</u>) is the <u>work done</u> (the energy transferred, measured in joules, J) <u>per coulomb of charge</u> that passes between <u>two points</u> in an electrical circuit. It's given by this formula:

2) So, the potential difference across an electrical component is the <u>amount of energy</u> that is transferred by that electrical component (e.g. to light and heat energy by a bulb) <u>per unit of charge</u>.

$$\text{P.D.} = \frac{\text{Work done}}{\text{Charge}}$$

3) <u>Voltage</u> and <u>potential difference</u> mean the <u>same thing</u>. You can use <u>either</u> in your exam and scoop up the marks (so long as you use it <u>correctly</u>).

I think it's about time you took charge...

Don't get confused by the words voltage and potential difference — they mean the <u>same thing</u>. Just remember that the potential difference is the work done between two points in a circuit, per unit of charge. Get those two formulas learned as well — examiners just love to test whether you understand them.

Circuits — The Basics

Formulas are mighty pretty and all, but you might have to design some <u>electrical circuits</u> as well one day. For that you're gonna need <u>circuit symbols</u>. Well, would you look at that... they're on this page.

Circuit Symbols <u>You Should Know</u> — <u>Learn Them Well</u>

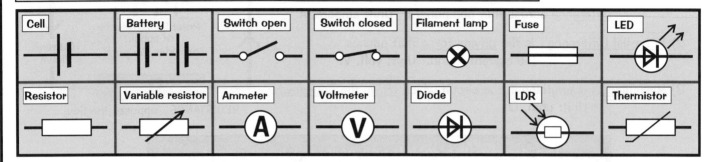

Cell	Battery	Switch open	Switch closed	Filament lamp	Fuse	LED

Resistor	Variable resistor	Ammeter	Voltmeter	Diode	LDR	Thermistor

The Standard Test Circuit

This is the circuit you use if you want to know the <u>resistance of a component</u>.
You find the resistance by measuring the <u>current through</u> and the <u>potential difference across</u> the component. It is absolutely the most <u>bog standard</u> circuit you could know. <u>So know it.</u>

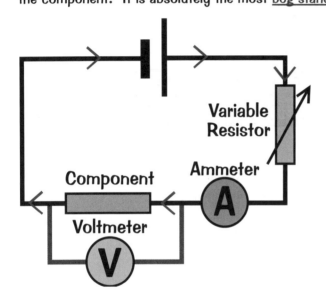

Variable Resistor

Component

Ammeter

Voltmeter

The Ammeter

1) Measures the <u>current</u> (in <u>amps</u>) flowing through the component.

2) Must be placed <u>in series</u> (see p.89).

3) Can be put <u>anywhere</u> in series in the <u>main circuit</u>, but <u>never</u> in parallel like the voltmeter.

The Voltmeter

1) Measures the <u>potential difference</u> (in <u>volts</u>) across the component.

2) Must be placed <u>in parallel</u> (see p.90) around the <u>component</u> under test — <u>NOT</u> around the variable resistor or the battery!

Five Important Points

1) This <u>very basic</u> circuit is used for testing <u>components</u>, and for getting <u>V-I graphs</u> from them (see next page).

2) The <u>component</u>, the <u>ammeter</u> and the <u>variable resistor</u> are all in <u>series</u>, which means they can be put in <u>any order</u> in the main circuit. The <u>voltmeter</u>, on the other hand, can only be placed <u>in parallel</u> around the <u>component under test</u>, as shown. Anywhere else is a definite <u>no-no</u>.

3) As you <u>vary</u> the <u>variable resistor</u> it alters the <u>current</u> flowing through the circuit.

4) This allows you to take several <u>pairs of readings</u> from the <u>ammeter</u> and <u>voltmeter</u>.

5) You can then <u>plot</u> these values for <u>current</u> and <u>voltage</u> on a <u>V-I graph</u> and find the <u>resistance</u>.

Measure gymnastics — use a vaultmeter...

The funny thing is — the <u>electrons</u> in circuits actually move from <u>−ve to +ve</u>... but scientists always think of <u>current</u> as flowing from <u>+ve to −ve</u>. Basically it's just because that's how the <u>early physicists</u> thought of it (before they found out about the electrons), and now it's become <u>convention</u>.

Resistance and V = I × R

With your current and your potential difference measured, you can now make some <u>sweet</u> graphs...

Three *Hideously Important* Potential Difference-Current Graphs

V-I graphs show how the <u>current</u> varies as you <u>change</u> the <u>potential difference</u> (P.D.). Learn these three real well:

Different Resistors

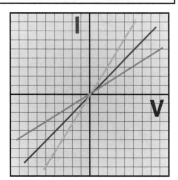

The current through a <u>resistor</u> (at constant temperature) is <u>directly proportional to P.D.</u> <u>Different resistors</u> have different <u>resistances</u>, hence the different <u>slopes</u>.

Filament Lamp

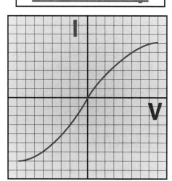

As the <u>temperature</u> of the filament <u>increases</u>, the <u>resistance increases</u>, hence the <u>curve</u>.

Diode

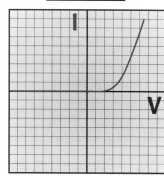

Current will only flow through a diode <u>in one direction</u>, as shown. The diode has very <u>high resistance</u> in the opposite direction.

Resistance Increases with Temperature

1) When an electrical charge flows through a resistor, some of the electrical energy is <u>transferred to heat energy</u> and the resistor gets <u>hot</u>.

2) This heat energy causes the <u>ions</u> in the conductor to <u>vibrate more</u>. With the ions jiggling around it's <u>more difficult</u> for the charge-carrying electrons to get through the resistor — the <u>current can't flow</u> as easily and the <u>resistance increases</u>.

3) For most resistors there is a <u>limit</u> to the amount of current that can flow. More current means an <u>increase</u> in <u>temperature</u>, which means an <u>increase</u> in <u>resistance</u>, which means the <u>current decreases</u> again.

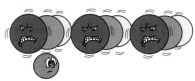

4) This is why the graph for the filament lamp <u>levels off</u> at high currents.

Resistance, Potential Difference *and* Current: V = I × R

Potential Difference = Current × Resistance

For the <u>straight-line graphs</u> above, the resistance of the component is <u>steady</u> and is equal to the <u>inverse</u> of the <u>gradient</u> of the line, or "<u>1/gradient</u>". In other words, the <u>steeper</u> the graph the <u>lower</u> the resistance.

If the graph <u>curves</u>, it means the resistance is <u>changing</u>. In that case R can be found for any point by taking the <u>pair of values</u> (V, I) from the graph and sticking them in the formula <u>R = V/I</u>. Easy.

EXAMPLE: Voltmeter V reads 6 V and resistor R is 4 Ω. What is the current through Ammeter A?

ANSWER: Use the formula triangle for V = I × R. We need to find I, so the version we need is I = V/R. The answer is then: I = 6 ÷ 4 = 1.5 A.

In the end you'll have to learn this — resistance is futile...

You have to be able to <u>interpret</u> potential difference-current graphs for your exam. Remember — the <u>steeper</u> the <u>slope</u>, the <u>lower</u> the <u>resistance</u>. And you need to know that formula inside out, back to front, upside down and in Swahili. It's the most important equation in electrics, bar none. (P.S. I might let you off the Swahili.)

88

Circuit Devices

You might consider yourself a bit of an <u>expert</u> in circuit components — you're enlightened about bulbs, you're switched on to switches... Just make sure you know these ones as well — they're a <u>little bit trickier</u>.

Current Only Flows in One Direction through a Diode

1) A diode is a special device made from <u>semiconductor</u> material such as <u>silicon</u>.
2) It is used to <u>regulate</u> the <u>potential difference</u> in circuits.
3) It lets current flow freely through it in <u>one direction</u>, but <u>not</u> in the other (i.e. there's a very high resistance in the <u>reverse</u> direction).
4) This turns out to be real useful in various <u>electronic circuits</u>.

Light-Emitting Diodes are Very Useful

1) A <u>light-emitting diode</u> (LED) emits light when a current flows through it in the <u>forward direction</u>.
2) LEDs are being used more and more as lighting, as they use a much <u>smaller current</u> than other forms of lighting.
3) LEDs indicate the presence of current in a circuit. They're often used in appliances (e.g. TVs) to show that they are <u>switched on</u>.
4) They're also used for the numbers on <u>digital clocks</u>, in <u>traffic lights</u> and in <u>remote controls</u>.

A Light-Dependent Resistor or "LDR" to You

1) An LDR is a resistor that is <u>dependent</u> on the <u>intensity</u> of <u>light</u>. Simple really.
2) In <u>bright light</u>, the resistance <u>falls</u>.
3) In <u>darkness</u>, the resistance is <u>highest</u>.
4) They have lots of applications including <u>automatic night lights</u>, outdoor lighting and <u>burglar detectors</u>.

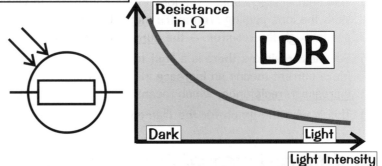

The Resistance of a Thermistor Decreases as Temperature Increases

1) A <u>thermistor</u> is a <u>temperature dependent</u> resistor.
2) In <u>hot</u> conditions, the resistance <u>drops</u>.
3) In <u>cool</u> conditions, the resistance goes <u>up</u>.
4) Thermistors make useful <u>temperature detectors</u>, e.g. <u>car engine</u> temperature sensors and electronic <u>thermostats</u>.

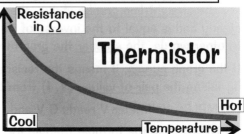

LDRs — Light-Dependent Rabbits...

LDRs are good triggers in security systems, because they can detect when the <u>light intensity</u> changes. So if a robber walks in front of a <u>beam of light</u> pointed at the LDR, the <u>resistance shoots up</u> and an alarm goes off.

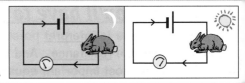

Series Circuits

You need to be able to tell the difference between series and parallel circuits <u>just by looking at them</u>. You also need to know the <u>rules</u> about what happens with both types. Read on.

Series Circuits — All or Nothing

1) In <u>series circuits</u>, the different components are connected <u>in a line</u>, <u>end to end</u>, between the +ve and −ve of the power supply (except for <u>voltmeters</u>, which are always connected <u>in parallel</u>, but they don't count as part of the circuit).

2) If you remove or disconnect <u>one</u> component, the circuit is <u>broken</u> and they all <u>stop</u>.

3) This is generally <u>not very handy</u>, and in practice <u>very few things</u> are connected in series.

1) Potential Difference is Shared:

In series circuits the <u>total P.D.</u> of the <u>supply</u> is <u>shared</u> between the various <u>components</u>. So the <u>voltages</u> round a series circuit <u>always add up</u> to equal the <u>source voltage</u>:

$$V = V_1 + V_2 + \ldots$$

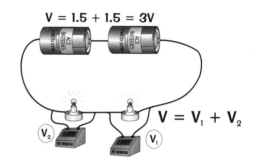

$V = 1.5 + 1.5 = 3V$

$V = V_1 + V_2$

2) Current is the Same Everywhere:

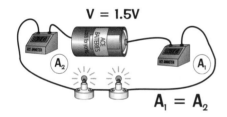

$V = 1.5V$

$A_1 = A_2$

1) In series circuits the <u>same current</u> flows through <u>all parts</u> of the circuit, i.e:

$$A_1 = A_2$$

2) The <u>size</u> of the current is determined by the <u>total P.D.</u> of the cells and the <u>total resistance</u> of the circuit: i.e. $I = V/R$

3) Resistance Adds Up:

1) In series circuits the <u>total resistance</u> is just the <u>sum</u> of all the resistances:

$$R = R_1 + R_2 + R_3$$

2) The <u>bigger</u> the <u>resistance</u> of a component, the bigger its <u>share</u> of the <u>total P.D.</u>

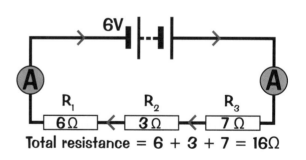

6V

R_1 R_2 R_3
6Ω   3Ω   7Ω

Total resistance = 6 + 3 + 7 = 16Ω

Cell Voltages Add Up:

1) There is a bigger potential difference when more cells are in series, provided the cells are all <u>connected</u> the <u>same way</u>.

2) For example when two batteries of voltage 1.5 V are <u>connected in series</u> they supply 3 V <u>between them</u>.

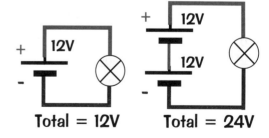

+ 12V

+ 12V
12V

Total = 12V   Total = 24V

Series circuits — they're no laughing matter...

If you connect a lamp to a battery, it lights up with a certain brightness. If you then add more identical lamps in series with the first one, they'll all light up <u>less brightly</u> than before. That's because in a series circuit the voltage is <u>shared out</u> between all the components. That doesn't happen in parallel circuits...

Parallel Circuits

Parallel circuits are much more <u>sensible</u> than series circuits and so they're much more <u>common</u> in <u>real life</u>. All the electrics in your house will be wired in parallel circuits.

Parallel Circuits — Independence and Isolation

1) In <u>parallel circuits</u>, each component is <u>separately</u> connected to the +ve and –ve of the <u>supply</u>.

2) If you remove or disconnect <u>one</u> of them, it will <u>hardly affect</u> the others at all.

3) This is <u>obviously</u> how <u>most</u> things must be connected, for example in <u>cars</u> and in <u>household electrics</u>. You have to be able to switch everything on and off <u>separately</u>.

1) P.D. is the Same Across All Components:

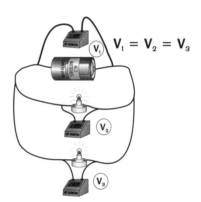

1) In parallel circuits <u>all</u> components get the <u>full source P.D.</u>, so the voltage is the <u>same</u> across all components:

$$V_1 = V_2 = V_3$$

2) This means that <u>identical bulbs</u> connected in parallel will all be at the <u>same brightness</u>.

2) Current is Shared Between Branches:

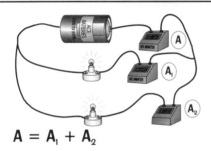

$$A = A_1 + A_2$$

1) In parallel circuits the <u>total current</u> flowing around the circuit is equal to the <u>total</u> of all the currents through the <u>separate components</u>.

$$A = A_1 + A_2 + ...$$

2) In a parallel circuit, there are <u>junctions</u> where the current either <u>splits</u> or <u>rejoins</u>. The total current going <u>into</u> a junction has to equal the total current <u>leaving</u>.

3) If two <u>identical components</u> are connected in parallel then the <u>same current</u> will flow through each component.

Voltmeters and Ammeters Are Exceptions to the Rule:

1) Ammeters and voltmeters are <u>exceptions</u> to the series and parallel rules.

2) Ammeters are <u>always</u> connected in <u>series</u> even in a parallel circuit.

3) Voltmeters are <u>always</u> connected in <u>parallel with a component</u> even in a series circuit.

A current shared — is a current halved...

Parallel circuits might look a bit scarier than series ones, but they're much more useful — and you don't have to learn as many equations for them (yay!). Remember: each branch has the <u>same voltage</u> across it, and the <u>total current</u> is <u>equal</u> to the <u>sum of the currents</u> through each of the branches.

Series and Parallel Circuits — Examples

It's not enough to know how circuits work in theory, it's important that you can calculate the currents, potential differences and resistances in a range of examples. It will be on the exam, so work through these examples now.

Example on Series Circuits

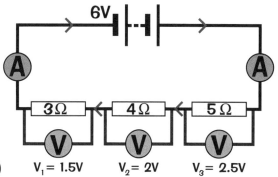

Potential differences add to equal the source P.D.:
1.5 + 2 + 2.5 = 6 V

Total resistance is the sum of the resistances in the circuit:
3 + 4 + 5 = 12 Ω

Current flowing through all parts of the circuit
= V/R = 6/12 = 0.5 A

(If an extra cell was added of P.D. 3 V then the P.D. across each resistor would increase and the current would increase too.)

$V_1 = 1.5V$ $V_2 = 2V$ $V_3 = 2.5V$

Christmas Fairy Lights are Often Wired in Series

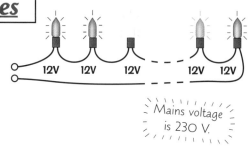

Christmas fairy lights are about the only real-life example of things connected in series, and we all know what a pain they are when the whole lot go out just because one of the bulbs is slightly dicky. The only advantage is that the bulbs can be very small because the total 230 V is shared out between them, so each bulb only has a small potential difference across it.

Mains voltage is 230 V.

Example on Parallel Circuits

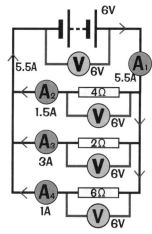

1) The P.D. across each resistor in the circuit is the same as the supply P.D. Each voltmeter will read 6 V.

2) The current through each resistor will be different because they have different values of resistance.

3) The current through the battery is the same as the sum of the other currents in the branches.
i.e. $A_1 = A_2 + A_3 + A_4 \Rightarrow A_1 = 1.5 + 3 + 1 = 5.5$ A

Everything Electrical in a Car is Connected in Parallel

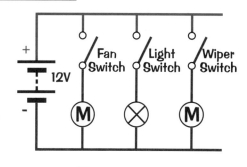

Parallel connection is essential in a car to give these two features:

1) Everything can be turned on and off separately.
2) Everything always gets the full voltage from the battery.

The only slight effect is that when you turn lots of things on the lights may go dim because the battery can't provide full voltage under heavy load. This is normally a very slight effect. You can spot the same thing at home when you turn a kettle on, if you watch very carefully.

Ⓜ is the symbol for a motor.

In a parallel universe — my car would start...

A lot of fairy lights are actually done on a parallel circuit these days — they have an adapter that brings the voltage down, so the lights can still be diddy but it doesn't matter if one of them blows. Cunning.

Revision Summary for Physics 2a

Well done — you've made it to the end of another section. There are loads of bits and bobs about forces, motion and electricity which you have to learn. The best way to find out what you know is to get stuck in to these lovely revision questions, which you're going to really enjoy (honest)...

1) What's the difference between speed and velocity?

2) Explain how to calculate speed from a distance-time graph.

3)* Write down the formula for acceleration. What's the acceleration of a soggy pea flicked from rest to a speed of 14 m/s in 0.4 seconds?

4) Sketch a typical velocity-time graph and point out all the important parts of it.

5) Explain how to find speed, distance and acceleration from a velocity-time graph.

6) Explain the difference between mass and weight. What units are they measured in?

7) If an object has zero resultant force on it, can it be moving? Can it be accelerating?

8)* Write down the formula relating resultant force and acceleration. A resultant force of 30 N pushes a trolley of mass 4 kg. What will be its acceleration?

9)* A skydiver has a mass of 75 kg. At 80 mph, the drag force on the skydiver is 650 N. Find the acceleration of the skydiver at 80 mph (take g = 10 N/kg).

10)* A yeti pushes a tree with a force of 120 N. What is the size of the reaction force that the Yeti feels pushing back at him?

11) What is "terminal velocity"?

12) What are the two different parts of the overall stopping distance of a car?

13)* Write down the formula for work done. A crazy dog drags a big branch 12 m over the next-door neighbour's front lawn, pulling with a force of 535 N. How much work was done?

14)* A 4 kg cheese is taken 30 m up a hill before being rolled back down again. If g = 10 N/kg, how much gravitational potential energy does the cheese have at the top of the hill?

15)* What's the formula for kinetic energy? Find the kinetic energy of a 78 kg sheep moving at 23 m/s.

16)* Calculate the kinetic energy of the same 78 kg sheep just as she hits the floor after falling through 20 m.

17)* A car of mass 1000 kg is travelling at a velocity of 2 m/s when a dazed and confused sheep runs out 5 m in front. If the driver immediately applies the maximum braking force of 395 N, can he avoid hitting it?

18) Write down the equation that relates the force on a spring and its extension.

19) What is the limit of proportionality?

20)* Calculate the power output of that 78 kg sheep when she runs 20 m up a staircase in 16.5 seconds.

21) Write down the formula for momentum. If the total momentum of a system before a collision is zero, what is the total momentum of the system after the collision?

22) What is the advantage of using regenerative braking systems?

23) Explain how seat belts, crumple zones, side impact bars and air bags are useful in a crash.

24) Describe the effect on the top speed of a car of adding a roof box. Explain your answer.

25) What causes the build-up of static electricity? Which particles move when static builds up?

26) True or false: the greater the resistance of an electrical component, the smaller the current through it?

27)* 240 C of charge is carried though a wire in a circuit in one minute. How much current flowed in the wire?

28) What formula relates work done, potential difference and charge?

29) Sketch typical potential difference-current graphs for:
a) a resistor, b) a filament lamp, c) a diode. Explain the shape of each graph.

30) Explain how resistance of a component changes with its temperature in terms of ions and electrons.

31)* What potential difference is required to push 2 A of current through a 0.6 Ω resistor?

32) Give three applications of LEDs.

33) Describe how the resistance of an LDR varies with light intensity. Give an application of an LDR.

34)* A 4 Ω bulb and a 6 Ω bulb are connected in series with a 12 V battery.
a) How much current flows through the 4 Ω bulb?
b) What is the potential difference over the 6 Ω bulb?
c) What would the potential difference over the 6 Ω bulb be if the two bulbs were connected in parallel?

* Answers on p.108.

Mains Electricity

Electric current is the <u>movement of charge carriers</u>. To transfer energy, it <u>doesn't matter which way</u> the charge carriers are going. That's why an <u>alternating current</u> works. Read on to find out more...

Mains Supply is AC, Battery Supply is DC

1) The UK mains supply is approximately <u>230 volts</u>.

2) It is an <u>AC supply</u> (alternating current), which means the current is <u>constantly</u> changing direction.

3) The frequency of the AC mains supply is <u>50 cycles per second</u> or <u>50 Hz</u> (hertz).

4) By contrast, cells and batteries supply <u>direct current</u> (DC). This just means that the current always keeps flowing in the <u>same direction</u>.

Electricity Supplies Can Be Shown on an Oscilloscope Screen

1) A <u>cathode ray oscilloscope</u> (CRO) is basically a snazzy <u>voltmeter</u>.

2) If you plug an <u>AC supply</u> into an oscilloscope, you get a '<u>trace</u>' on the screen that shows how the voltage of the supply changes with <u>time</u>. The trace goes up and down in a <u>regular pattern</u> — some of the time it's positive and some of the time it's negative.

3) If you plug in a <u>DC supply</u>, the trace you get is just a <u>straight line</u>.

4) The <u>vertical height</u> of the AC trace at any point shows the <u>input voltage</u> at that point. By measuring the height of the trace you can find the potential difference of the AC supply.

5) For DC it's a <u>lot simpler</u> — the voltage is just the distance from the <u>straight line trace</u> to the centre line.

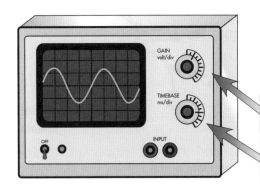

The GAIN dial controls how many volts each centimetre division represents on the vertical axis.

The TIMEBASE dial controls how many milliseconds (1 ms = 0.001 s) each division represents on the horizontal axis.

Learn How to Read an Oscilloscope Trace

DC supply

A <u>DC</u> source is always at the <u>same voltage</u>, so you get a <u>straight line</u>.

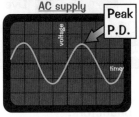

AC supply   Peak P.D.

An <u>AC</u> source gives a <u>regularly repeating wave</u>. From that, you can work out the <u>period</u> and the <u>frequency</u> of the supply.

You work out the frequency using:

$$\text{Frequency (Hz)} = \frac{1}{\text{Time period (s)}}$$

EXAMPLE: The trace below comes from an oscilloscope with the timebase set to 5 ms/div. Find: a) the time period, and b) the frequency of the AC supply.

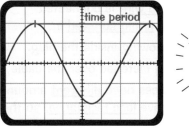

time period

Time period = the time to complete one cycle. 1 ms = 0.001 s.

<u>ANSWER:</u> a) To find the time period, measure the horizontal distance between two peaks. The time period of the signal is 6 divisions. Multiply by the timebase:
Time period = 5 ms × 6 = <u>0.03 s</u>

b) Using the frequency formula on the left:
Frequency = 1/0.03 = <u>33 Hz</u>

I wish my bank account had a gain dial...

Because mains power is AC, its current can be increased or decreased using a device called a <u>transformer</u>. The lower the current in power transmission lines, the less energy is wasted as heat.

Electricity in the Home

Now then, did you know... electricity is <u>dangerous</u>. It can kill you. Well just watch out for it, that's all.

Hazards <u>in the</u> Home — <u>Eliminate Them Before They Eliminate You</u>

A likely <u>exam question</u> will show you a picture of domestic bliss but with various <u>electrical hazards</u> in the picture such as kids shoving their fingers into sockets and stuff like that, and they'll ask you to <u>list all the hazards</u>. This should be mostly <u>common sense</u>, but it won't half help if you already know some of the likely hazards, so learn these 9 examples:

1) <u>Long cables</u>.
2) <u>Frayed cables</u>.
3) <u>Cables</u> in contact with something <u>hot</u> or <u>wet</u>.
4) <u>Water near sockets</u>.
5) <u>Shoving</u> things into sockets.

6) <u>Damaged plugs</u>.
7) <u>Too many</u> plugs into one socket.
8) Lighting sockets <u>without bulbs in</u>.
9) Appliances without their <u>covers</u> on.

Most Cables <u>Have Three Separate</u> Wires

1) Most electrical appliances are connected to the mains supply by <u>three-core</u> cables. This means that they have <u>three wires</u> inside them, each with a <u>core of copper</u> and a <u>coloured plastic coating</u>.
2) The brown <u>LIVE WIRE</u> in a mains supply alternates between a <u>HIGH +VE AND –VE VOLTAGE</u>.
3) The blue <u>NEUTRAL WIRE</u> is always at <u>0V</u>. Electricity normally flows in and out through the live and neutral wires only.
4) The green and yellow <u>EARTH WIRE</u> is for protecting the wiring, and for safety — it works together with a fuse to prevent fire and shocks. It is attached to the metal casing of the appliance and <u>carries the electricity to earth</u> (and away from you) should something go wrong and the live or neutral wires touch the metal case.

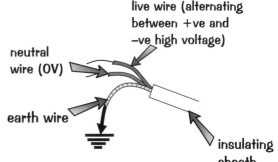

neutral wire (0V)

live wire (alternating between +ve and –ve high voltage)

earth wire

insulating sheath

Three-Pin Plugs <u>and Cables</u> — <u>Learn the Safety Features</u>

Get the <u>Wiring Right</u>

1) The <u>right coloured wire</u> is connected to each pin, and <u>firmly screwed</u> in.
2) <u>No bare wires</u> showing inside the plug.
3) <u>Cable grip</u> tightly fastened over the cable <u>outer layer</u>.
4) Different appliances need <u>different</u> amounts of electrical energy. <u>Thicker</u> cables have <u>less resistance</u>, so they carry <u>more current</u>.

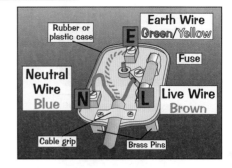

Rubber or plastic case

Earth Wire Green/Yellow

E

Fuse

Neutral Wire Blue

N

L

Live Wire Brown

Cable grip

Brass Pins

Plug <u>Features</u>

1) The <u>metal parts</u> are made of copper or brass because these are <u>very good conductors</u>.
2) The case, cable grip and cable insulation are made of <u>rubber</u> or <u>plastic</u> because they're really good <u>insulators</u>, and <u>flexible</u> too.
3) This all keeps the electricity flowing <u>where it should</u>.

CGP books are ACE — well, I had to get a plug in somewhere...

Pure water doesn't conduct electricity, but water (usually) has mineral salts dissolved in it. These carry the charge around really well, making it a <u>very good conductor</u>. So don't blow dry your hair in the bath, OK?

Fuses and Earthing

Questions about fuses are an exam favourite because they cover a whole barrel of fun — electrical current, resistance, energy transfers and electrical safety. Learn this page and make sure you've got it sussed.

Earthing and Fuses Prevent Electrical Overloads

The earth wire and fuse (or circuit breaker) are included in electrical appliances for safety and work together like this:

1) If a fault develops in which the live wire somehow touches the metal case, then because the case is earthed, too great a current flows in through the live wire, through the case and out down the earth wire.

2) This surge in current melts the fuse (or trips the circuit breaker in the live wire) when the amount of current is greater than the fuse rating. This cuts off the live supply and breaks the circuit.

3) This isolates the whole appliance, making it impossible to get an electric shock from the case. It also prevents the risk of fire caused by the heating effect of a large current.

4) As well as people, fuses and earthing are there to protect the circuits and wiring in your appliances from getting fried if there is a current surge.

5) Fuses should be rated as near as possible but just higher than the normal operating current.

6) The larger the current, the thicker the cable you need to carry it. That's why the fuse rating needed for cables usually increases with cable thickness.

Insulating Materials Make Appliances "Double Insulated"

All appliances with metal cases are usually "earthed" to reduce the danger of electric shock. "Earthing" just means the case must be attached to an earth wire. An earthed conductor can never become live. If the appliance has a plastic casing and no metal parts showing then it's said to be double insulated.

Anything with double insulation like that doesn't need an earth wire — just a live and neutral. Cables that only carry the live and neutral wires are known as two-core cables.

Circuit Breakers Have Some Advantages Over Fuses

1) Circuit breakers are an electrical safety device used in some circuits. Like fuses, they protect the circuit from damage if too much current flows.

2) When circuit breakers detect a surge in current in a circuit, they break the circuit by opening a switch.

3) A circuit breaker (and the circuit they're in) can easily be reset by flicking a switch on the device. This makes them more convenient than fuses — which have to be replaced once they've melted.

4) They are, however, a lot more expensive to buy than fuses.

5) One type of circuit breaker used instead of a fuse and an earth wire is a Residual Current Circuit Breakers (RCCBs):

   a) Normally exactly the same current flows through the live and neutral wires. If somebody touches the live wire, a small but deadly current will flow through them to the earth. This means the neutral wire carries less current than the live wire. The RCCB detects this difference in current and quickly cuts off the power by opening a switch.

   b) They also operate much faster than fuses — they break the circuit as soon as there is a current surge — no time is wasted waiting for the current to melt a fuse. This makes them safer.

   c) RCCBs even work for small current changes that might not be large enough to melt a fuse. Since even small current changes could be fatal, this means RCCBs are more effective at protecting against electrocution.

Why are earth wires green and yellow — when mud is brown..?

All these safety precautions mean it's pretty difficult to get electrocuted on modern appliances. But that's only so long as they are in good condition and you're not doing something really stupid. Watch out for frayed wires, don't overload plugs, and for goodness sake don't use a knife to get toast out of a toaster when it is switched on.

Energy and Power in Circuits

Electricity is just another form of <u>energy</u> — which means that it is always <u>conserved</u>.

Energy is Transferred from Cells and Other Sources

Anything which <u>supplies electricity</u> is also supplying <u>energy</u>.

So cells, batteries, generators, etc. all <u>transfer energy</u> to components in the circuit:

| <u>Motion</u>: motors | <u>Light</u>: light bulbs | <u>Heat</u>: Hair dryers/kettles | <u>Sound</u>: speakers |

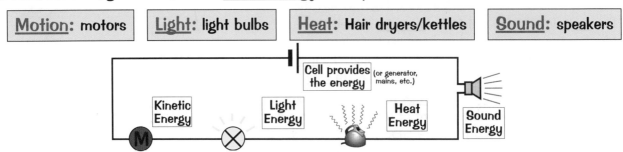

All Resistors Produce Heat When a Current Flows Through Them

1) Whenever a <u>current</u> flows through anything with <u>electrical resistance</u> (which is pretty much everything) then <u>electrical energy</u> is converted into <u>heat energy</u>.

2) The <u>more current</u> that flows, the more heat is produced.

3) A <u>bigger voltage</u> means more heating because it pushes more current through.

4) <u>Filament bulbs</u> work by passing a current through a very <u>thin wire</u>, heating it up so much that it glows. Rather obviously, they waste a lot of energy as <u>heat</u>.

If an Appliance is Efficient it Wastes Less Energy

All this energy wasted as heat can get a little <u>depressing</u> — but there is a solution.

1) When you buy electrical appliances you can choose to buy ones that are more <u>energy efficient</u>.

2) These appliances transfer more of their <u>total electrical energy output to useful energy</u>.

Not an energy efficient lamp.

3) For example, less energy is wasted as heat in power-saving lamps such as <u>compact fluorescent lamps</u> (CFLs) and <u>light emitting diodes</u> (p.88) than in ordinary filament bulbs.

4) Unfortunately, they do <u>cost more to buy</u>, but over time the money you <u>save</u> on your electricity bills pays you back for the initial investment.

Power of Appliances

The total energy transferred by an appliance depends on <u>how long</u> the appliance is on and its <u>power</u>.

The power of an appliance is the <u>energy</u> that it uses <u>per second</u>.

Energy Transferred = Power × time

$$\frac{E}{P \times t}$$

For example, if a 2.5 kW kettle is on for 5 minutes, the energy transferred by the kettle in this time is 300 × 2500 = 750 000 J = 750 kJ. (5 minutes = 300 s).

Ohm's girlfriend was a vixen — he couldn't resistor...

The equation for <u>power</u> is a real simple one, but it's <u>absolutely essential</u> that you've got it hard-wired into your memory. Remember: power is energy transferred per second. Power is energy transferred per second. Power is energy transferred per second....

Power and Energy Change

You can think about <u>electrical circuits</u> in terms of <u>energy transfer</u> — the charge carriers take charge around the circuit, and when they go through an electrical component energy is transferred to make the component work.

Electrical Power and Fuse Ratings

1) The formula for <u>electrical power</u> is:

> POWER = CURRENT × POTENTIAL DIFFERENCE

$$P = I \times V$$

2) You can use this equation to work out the fuse that should be used in an appliance. To work out the size of the <u>fuse</u> needed, you need to work out the <u>current</u> that the item will normally use:

> **EXAMPLE:** A 1 kW hair dryer is connected to a 230 V supply. Find the fuse needed.
> **ANSWER:** I = P/V = 1000/230 = 4.3 A. Normally, the fuse should be rated just a little higher than the normal current, so a 5 amp fuse is ideal for this one.

The Potential Difference is the Energy Transferred per Charge Passed

1) When an electrical <u>charge</u> (Q) goes through a <u>change</u> in potential difference (V), then <u>energy</u> (E) is <u>transferred</u>.

2) Energy is <u>supplied</u> to the charge at the <u>power source</u> to 'raise' it through a potential.

3) The charge <u>gives up</u> this energy when it '<u>falls</u>' through any <u>potential drop</u> in <u>components</u> elsewhere in the circuit.

The formula is real simple:

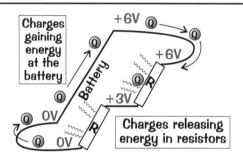

Charges gaining energy at the battery

Charges releasing energy in resistors

> Energy transformed = Charge × Potential difference

4) The <u>bigger</u> the <u>change</u> in P.D. (or voltage.), the <u>more energy</u> is transferred for a <u>given amount of charge</u> passing through the circuit.

5) That means that a battery with a <u>bigger voltage</u> will supply <u>more energy</u> to the circuit for every <u>coulomb</u> of charge which flows round it, because the charge is raised up "<u>higher</u>" at the start (see above diagram) — and as the diagram shows, <u>more energy</u> will be <u>dissipated</u> in the circuit too.

> **EXAMPLE:** The motor in an electric toothbrush is attached to a 3 V battery.
> If a current of 0.8 A flows through the motor for 3 minutes:
>
> a) Calculate the total charge passed.
>
> b) Calculate the energy transformed by the motor.
>
> c) Explain why the kinetic energy output of the motor will be less than your answer to b).
>
> **ANSWER:** a) Use the formula (p.85) Q = I × t = 0.8 × (3 × 60) = <u>144 C</u>
>
> b) Use E = Q × V = 144 × 3 = <u>432 J</u>
>
> c) The motor won't be 100% efficient. Some of the energy will be transformed into <u>sound and heat</u>.

You have the power — now use your potential...

Ok, another two formulas to learn. By this point you're probably experiencing a little bit of formula fatigue, but trust me, you will be glad that you learned them all. Try to think about exactly what each one means and how they work together — things are a lot easier to memorise if you have a real understanding of why they are there.

Atomic Structure

Ernest Rutherford didn't just pick the nuclear model of the atom out of thin air. It all started with a Greek fella called Democritus in the 5th Century BC. He thought that all matter, whatever it was, was made up of identical lumps called "atomos". And that's about as far as the theory got until the 1800s...

Rutherford Scattering and the Demise of the Plum Pudding

1) In 1804 John Dalton agreed with Democritus that matter was made up of tiny spheres ("atoms") that couldn't be broken up, but he reckoned that each element was made up of a different type of "atom".

2) Nearly 100 years later, J J Thomson discovered that electrons could be removed from atoms. So Dalton's theory wasn't quite right (atoms could be broken up). Thomson suggested that atoms were spheres of positive charge with tiny negative electrons stuck in them like plums in a plum pudding.

3) That "plum pudding" theory didn't last very long though. In 1909 Rutherford and Marsden tried firing a beam of alpha particles (see p.100) at thin gold foil. They expected that the positively charged alpha particles would be slightly deflected by the electrons in the plum pudding model.

4) However, most of the alpha particles just went straight through, but the odd one came straight back at them, which was frankly a bit of a shocker for Rutherford and his pal.

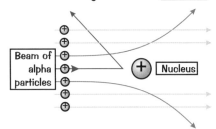

5) Being pretty clued-up guys, Rutherford and Marsden realised this meant that most of the mass of the atom was concentrated at the centre in a tiny nucleus. They also realised that the nucleus must have a large positive charge, since it repelled the positive alpha particles by large angles.

6) It also showed that most of an atom is just empty space, which is also a bit of a shocker when you think about it.

Rutherford and Marsden Came Up with the Nuclear Model of the Atom

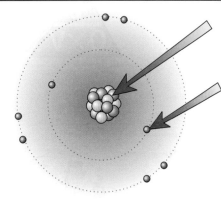

The nucleus is tiny but it makes up most of the mass of the atom. It contains protons (which are positively charged) and neutrons (which are neutral) — which gives it an overall positive charge.

The rest of the atom is mostly empty space. The negative electrons whizz round the outside of the nucleus really fast. They give the atom its overall size — the radius of the atom's nucleus is about 10 000 times smaller than the radius of the atom. Crikey.

Learn the relative charges and masses of each particle:

PARTICLE	MASS	CHARGE
Proton	1	+1
Neutron	1	0
Electron	$\frac{1}{2000}$	-1

Number of Protons Equals Number of Electrons

1) Atoms have no charge overall.
2) The charge on an electron is the same size as the charge on a proton — but opposite.
3) This means the number of protons always equals the number of electrons in a neutral atom.
4) If some electrons are added or removed, the atom becomes a charged particle called an ion.

And I always thought Kate Moss was the best model...

The nuclear model is just one way of thinking about the atom. It works really well for explaining a lot of physical properties of different elements, but it's certainly not the whole story. Other bits of science are explained using different models of the atom. The beauty of it though is that no one model is more right than the others.

Atoms and Radiation

You have just entered the subatomic realm — now stuff starts to get real interesting...

Isotopes are Different Forms of the Same Element

1) Isotopes are atoms with the same number of protons but a different number of neutrons.

2) Hence they have the same atomic number, but different mass numbers.

3) Atomic number is the number of protons in an atom. Mass number is the number of protons + the number of neutrons in an atom.

4) Carbon-12 and carbon-14 are good examples of isotopes: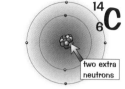

5) Most elements have different isotopes, but there's usually only one or two stable ones.

6) The other isotopes tend to be radioactive, which means they decay into other elements and give out radiation.

Radioactivity is a Totally Random Process

1) Radioactive substances give out radiation from the nuclei of their atoms — no matter what is done to them.

2) This process is entirely random. This means that if you have 1000 unstable nuclei, you can't say when any one of them is going to decay, and neither can you do anything at all to make a decay happen. It's completely unaffected by physical conditions like temperature or by any sort of chemical bonding etc.

3) Radioactive substances spit out one or more of the three types of radiation, alpha, beta or gamma (see next page).

Background Radiation Comes from Many Sources

Background radiation is radiation that is present at all times, all around us, wherever you go. The background radiation we receive comes from:

1) Radioactivity of naturally occurring unstable isotopes which are all around us — in the air, in food, in building materials and in the rocks under our feet.

2) Radiation from space, which is known as cosmic rays. These come mostly from the Sun.

3) Radiation due to man-made sources, e.g. fallout from nuclear weapons tests, nuclear accidents (such as Chernobyl) or dumped nuclear waste.

The RELATIVE PROPORTIONS of background radiation:

- 51% Radon gas
- 10% Cosmic rays
- 12% Food
- 12% Medical X-rays
- 14% Rocks and Building materials
- Just 1% from the Nuclear Industry

Radiation Dose Depends on Location and Occupation

How likely you are to suffer damage if you're exposed to nuclear radiation depends on the radiation dose. Radiation dose depends on the type and amount of radiation you've been exposed to. The higher the radiation dose, the more at risk you are of developing cancer. The amount of radiation you're exposed to (and hence your radiation dose) can be affected by your location and occupation.

1) Certain underground rocks (e.g. granite) can cause higher levels at the surface, especially if they release radioactive radon gas, which tends to get trapped inside people's houses.

2) At high altitudes (e.g. in jet planes) the background radiation increases because of more exposure to cosmic rays. That means commercial pilots have an increased risk of getting some types of cancer.

3) Underground (e.g. in mines, etc.) it increases because of the rocks all around, posing a risk to miners.

4) Nuclear industry workers and uranium miners are typically exposed to 10 times the normal amount of radiation. They wear protective clothing and face masks to stop them from touching or inhaling the radioactive material, and monitor their radiation doses with special radiation badges and regular check-ups.

5) Radiographers work in hospitals using ionising radiation and so have a higher risk of radiation exposure. They wear lead aprons and stand behind lead screens to protect them from prolonged exposure to radiation.

Completely random — just like your revision shouldn't be...

It's the number of protons which decides what element something is, then the number of neutrons decides what isotope of that element it is. And it's unstable isotopes which undergo radioactive decay.

Ionising Radiation

Alpha (α) Beta (β) Gamma (γ) — there's a short alphabet of radiation for you to learn here. And it's all <u>ionising</u>.

Alpha Particles <u>are</u> Helium Nuclei

1) An <u>alpha</u> particle is <u>two neutrons</u> and <u>two protons</u> — the same as a <u>helium nucleus</u>.
2) They are relatively <u>big</u> and <u>heavy</u> and <u>slow moving</u>.
3) They therefore <u>don't</u> penetrate very far into materials and are <u>stopped quickly</u>, even when travelling through <u>air</u>.
4) Because of their size they are <u>strongly ionising</u>, which just means they <u>bash into</u> a lot of atoms and <u>knock electrons off them</u> before they slow down, which creates lots of ions — hence the term "<u>ionising</u>".

Beta Particles <u>are</u> Electrons

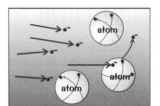

1) Beta particles are <u>in between</u> alpha and gamma in terms of their <u>properties</u>.
2) They move <u>quite</u> fast and they are <u>quite</u> small (they're electrons).
3) They <u>penetrate moderately</u> into materials before colliding, have a <u>long range</u> in air, and are <u>moderately ionising</u> too.
4) For every <u>β-particle</u> emitted, a <u>neutron</u> turns to a <u>proton</u> in the nucleus.
5) A <u>β-particle</u> is simply an <u>electron</u>, with virtually no mass and a charge of –1.

<u>You need to be able to</u> Balance Nuclear Equations

You can write alpha and beta decays as <u>nuclear equations</u>. Watch out for the <u>mass and atomic numbers</u> — they have to <u>balance up</u> on both sides.

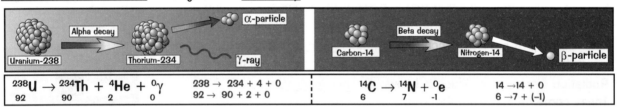

$$^{238}_{92}U \rightarrow\ ^{234}_{90}Th +\ ^{4}_{2}He +\ ^{0}_{0}\gamma \qquad 238 \rightarrow 234+4+0 \qquad 92 \rightarrow 90+2+0$$

$$^{14}_{6}C \rightarrow\ ^{14}_{7}N +\ ^{0}_{-1}e \qquad 14 \rightarrow 14+0 \qquad 6 \rightarrow 7+(-1)$$

Gamma Rays <u>are Very Short Wavelength</u> EM Waves

1) Gamma rays are the <u>opposite</u> of alpha particles in a way.
2) They <u>penetrate far into materials</u> without being stopped and pass <u>straight through air</u>.
3) This means they are <u>weakly</u> ionising because they tend to <u>pass through</u> rather than collide with atoms. Eventually they <u>hit something</u> and do <u>damage</u>.
4) Gamma rays have <u>no mass</u> and <u>no charge</u>.

Alpha <u>and</u> Beta <u>Particles are Deflected</u> by Electric <u>and</u> Magnetic Fields

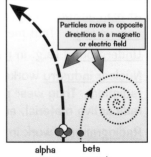

1) Alpha particles have a <u>positive charge</u>, beta particles have a <u>negative charge</u>.
2) When travelling through a <u>magnetic</u> or <u>electric field</u>, both alpha and beta particles will be <u>deflected</u>. They're deflected in <u>opposite directions</u> because of their <u>opposite charge</u>.
3) Alpha particles have a <u>larger charge</u> than beta particles, and feel a <u>greater force</u> in magnetic and electric fields. But they're <u>deflected less</u> because they have a <u>much greater mass</u>.
4) <u>Gamma radiation</u> is an electromagnetic (EM) wave and has <u>no charge</u>, so it <u>doesn't get deflected</u> by electric or magnetic fields.

I once beta particle — it cried for ages...

So, when a nucleus decays by <u>alpha</u> emission, its <u>atomic number</u> goes down by <u>two</u> and its <u>mass number</u> goes down by <u>four</u>. <u>Beta</u> emission increases the atomic number by <u>one</u> (the mass number <u>doesn't change</u>).

Half-Life

The <u>unit</u> for measuring <u>radioactivity</u> is the <u>becquerel</u> (Bq). 1 Bq means <u>one nucleus decaying per second</u>.

The Radioactivity of a Sample Always Decreases Over Time

1) This is <u>pretty obvious</u> when you think about it. Each time a <u>decay</u> happens and an alpha, beta or gamma is given out, it means one more <u>radioactive nucleus</u> has <u>disappeared</u>.

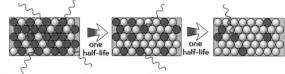

2) Obviously, as the <u>unstable nuclei</u> all steadily disappear, the <u>activity</u> (the number of nuclei that decay per second) will <u>decrease</u>. So the <u>older</u> a sample becomes, the <u>less radiation</u> it will emit.

3) <u>How quickly</u> the activity <u>drops off</u> varies a lot. For <u>some</u> substances it takes <u>just a few microseconds</u> before nearly all the unstable nuclei have <u>decayed</u>, whilst for others it can take <u>millions of years</u>.

4) The problem with trying to <u>measure</u> this is that <u>the activity never reaches zero</u>, which is why we have to use the idea of <u>half-life</u> to measure how quickly the activity <u>drops off</u>.

5) Learn this <u>definition</u> of <u>half-life</u>:

6) In other words, it is the <u>time it takes</u> for the <u>count rate</u> (the number of radioactive emissions detected per unit of time) from a sample containing the isotope to <u>fall to half its initial level</u>.

> **HALF-LIFE is the AVERAGE TIME it takes for the NUMBER OF NUCLEI in a RADIOACTIVE ISOTOPE SAMPLE to HALVE.**

7) A <u>short half-life</u> means the <u>activity falls quickly</u>, because <u>lots</u> of the nuclei decay <u>quickly</u>.

8) A <u>long half-life</u> means the activity <u>falls more slowly</u> because <u>most</u> of the nuclei don't decay <u>for a long time</u> — they just sit there, <u>basically unstable</u>, but kind of <u>biding their time</u>.

Do Half-life Questions Step by Step

Half-life is maybe a little confusing, but exam calculations are <u>straightforward</u> so long as you do them slowly, <u>STEP BY STEP</u>. Like this one:

<u>A VERY SIMPLE EXAMPLE:</u> The activity of a radioisotope is 640 cpm (counts per minute). Two hours later it has fallen to 80 cpm. Find the half-life of the sample.

<u>ANSWER:</u> You must go through it in <u>short simple steps</u> like this:

INITIAL count:	(÷2)→	after ONE half-life:	(÷2)→	after TWO half-lives:	(÷2)→	after THREE half-lives:
640		320		160		80

Notice the careful <u>step-by-step method</u>, which tells us it takes <u>three half-lives</u> for the activity to fall from 640 to 80. Hence <u>two hours</u> represents three half-lives, so the <u>half-life</u> is 120 mins ÷ 3 = <u>40 minutes</u>.

Finding the Half-life of a Sample Using a Graph

1) The data for the graph will usually be <u>several readings</u> of <u>count rate</u> taken with a <u>G-M tube and counter</u>.

2) The <u>graph</u> will always be <u>shaped</u> like the one shown.

3) The <u>half-life</u> is found from the graph by finding the <u>time interval</u> on the <u>bottom axis</u> corresponding to a <u>halving</u> of the <u>activity</u> on the <u>vertical axis</u>. Easy peasy really.

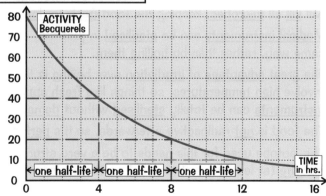

Half-life of a box of chocolates — about five minutes...

For <u>medical applications</u>, you need to use isotopes that have a <u>suitable half-life</u>. A radioactive tracer needs to have a short half-life to minimise the risk of damage to the patient. A source for sterilising equipment needs to have a long half-life, so you don't have to replace it too often (see next page).

Uses of Radiation

Radiation gets a lot of bad press, but the fact is it's essential for things like <u>modern medicine</u>. Read on chaps...

Smoke <u>Detectors</u> — Use α-<u>Radiation</u>

1) A <u>weak</u> source of <u>alpha</u> radiation is placed in the detector, close to <u>two electrodes</u>.

2) The source causes <u>ionisation</u>, and a <u>current</u> flows between the electrodes.

3) If there is a fire then smoke will <u>absorb</u> the radiation — so the current stops and the <u>alarm sounds</u>.

Tracers <u>in Medicine</u> — <u>Always Short Half-Life</u> β <u>or</u> γ <u>-Emitters</u>

1) Certain <u>radioactive isotopes</u> can be <u>injected</u> into people (or they can just <u>swallow</u> them) and their progress <u>around the body</u> can be followed using an external <u>detector</u>. A computer converts the reading to a <u>display</u> showing where the <u>strongest reading</u> is coming from.

2) A well-known example is the use of <u>iodine-131</u>, which is absorbed by the <u>thyroid gland</u> just like normal iodine-127, but it gives out <u>radiation</u> which can be <u>detected</u> to indicate whether the thyroid gland is <u>taking in iodine</u> as it should.

Gamma Rays

G-M tubes Ltd.

Iodine-131 collecting in the thyroid gland

3) <u>All isotopes</u> which are taken <u>into the body</u> must be <u>GAMMA or BETA</u> emitters (never alpha), so that the radiation <u>passes out of the body</u> — and they should only last <u>a few hours</u>, so that the radioactivity inside the patient <u>quickly disappears</u> (i.e. they should have a <u>short half-life</u>).

<u>Radiotherapy</u> — <u>the Treatment of Cancer Using</u> γ-<u>Rays</u>

1) Since high doses of gamma rays will <u>kill all living cells</u>, they can be used to <u>treat cancers</u>.

2) The gamma rays have to be <u>directed carefully</u> and at just the right <u>dosage</u> so as to kill the <u>cancer cells</u> without damaging too many <u>normal cells</u>.

3) However, a <u>fair bit of damage</u> is <u>inevitably</u> done to <u>normal cells</u>, which makes the patient feel <u>very ill</u>. But if the cancer is <u>successfully killed off</u> in the end, then it's worth it.

<u>Sterilisation</u> of <u>Food</u> and <u>Surgical Instruments Using</u> γ -<u>Rays</u>

1) <u>Food</u> can be exposed to a <u>high dose</u> of <u>gamma rays</u> which will <u>kill</u> all <u>microbes</u>, keeping the food <u>fresh for longer</u>.

2) <u>Medical instruments</u> can be <u>sterilised</u> in just the same way, rather than by <u>boiling them</u>.

unsterilised — Gamma source — sterilised

3) The great <u>advantage</u> of <u>irradiation</u> over boiling is that it doesn't involve <u>high temperatures</u>, so things like <u>fresh apples</u> or <u>plastic instruments</u> can be totally <u>sterilised</u> without <u>damaging</u> them.

4) The food is <u>not</u> radioactive afterwards, so it's <u>perfectly safe</u> to eat.

5) The isotope used for this needs to be a <u>very strong</u> emitter of <u>gamma rays</u> with a <u>reasonably long</u> <u>half-life</u> (at least several months) so that it doesn't need <u>replacing</u> too often.

<u>Ionising radiation</u> — <u>just what the doctor ordered...</u>

Radiation has many important uses — especially in <u>medicine</u>. Make sure you know why each application uses a particular <u>isotope</u> according to its half-life and the type of radiation it gives out.

Radioactivity Safety

When <u>Marie Curie</u> discovered the radioactive properties of <u>radium</u> in 1898, nobody knew about its dangers. Radium was used to make glow-in-the-dark watches and many <u>watch dial painters</u> developed cancer as a result.

Radiation *Harms* Living Cells

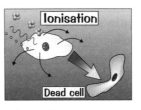
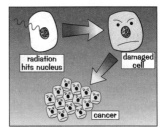

1) <u>Alpha</u>, <u>beta</u> and <u>gamma</u> radiation will cheerfully <u>enter living cells</u> and <u>collide with molecules</u>.

2) These collisions cause <u>ionisation</u>, which <u>damages or destroys</u> the <u>molecules</u>.

3) <u>Lower doses</u> tend to cause <u>minor damage</u> without <u>killing</u> the cell.

4) This can give rise to <u>mutant cells</u> which <u>divide uncontrollably</u>. This is <u>cancer</u>.

5) <u>Higher doses</u> tend to <u>kill cells completely</u>, which causes <u>radiation sickness</u> if a lot of body cells <u>all get blatted at once</u>.

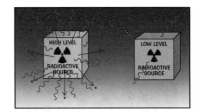

6) The <u>extent</u> of the harmful effects depends on <u>two things</u>:

   a) <u>How much exposure</u> you have to the radiation.

   b) The <u>energy and penetration</u> of the radiation, since <u>some types</u> are <u>more hazardous</u> than others, of course.

Outside *the Body,* β *and* γ–Sources *are the* Most Dangerous

This is because <u>beta and gamma</u> can get <u>inside</u> to the delicate <u>organs</u>, whereas alpha is much less dangerous because it <u>can't penetrate the skin</u>.

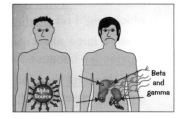

Inside *the Body, an* α-Source *is the* Most Dangerous

<u>Inside the body</u> alpha sources do all their damage in a <u>very localised area</u>. Beta and gamma sources on the other hand are <u>less dangerous</u> inside the body because they mostly <u>pass straight out</u> without doing much damage.

You Need to *Learn* About These *Safety Precautions*

Obviously radioactive materials need to be handled <u>carefully</u>. But in the exam they might ask you to <u>evaluate some specific precautions</u> that should be taken when <u>handling radioactive materials</u>.

1) When conducting experiments, use radioactive sources for as <u>short a time</u> as possible so your <u>exposure</u> is kept to a <u>minimum</u>.

2) <u>Never</u> allow <u>skin contact</u> with a source. Always handle with <u>tongs</u>.

3) Hold the source at <u>arm's length</u> to keep it <u>as far</u> from the body <u>as possible</u>. This will decrease the amount of radiation that hits you, especially for alpha particles as they <u>don't travel far in air</u>.

4) Keep the source <u>pointing away</u> from the body and <u>avoid looking directly at it</u>.

5) <u>Lead</u> absorbs all three types of radiation (though a lot of it is needed to stop gamma radiation completely). <u>Always</u> store radioactive sources in a <u>lead box</u> and put them away <u>as soon</u> as the experiment is <u>over</u>. Medical professionals who work with radiation <u>every day</u> (such as radiographers) wear <u>lead aprons</u> and stand behind <u>lead screens</u> for extra protection because of its radiation absorbing properties.

6) When someone needs an **X-ray** or radiotherapy, only the area of the body that <u>needs to be treated</u> is exposed to radiation. The rest of the body is <u>protected with lead</u> or other <u>radiation absorbing</u> materials.

Radiation sickness — well yes, it does all get a bit tedious...

Sadly, much of our knowledge of the harmful effects of radiation has come as a result of <u>devastating events</u> such as the <u>atomic bombing of Japan</u> in 1945. In the months following the bombs, thousands suffered from <u>radiation sickness</u> — the symptoms of which include nausea, fatigue, skin burns, hair loss and, in serious cases, death. In the <u>long term</u>, the area has experienced increased rates of cancer, particularly <u>leukaemia</u>.

Nuclear Fission and Fusion

Unstable isotopes aren't just good for medicine — with the right set-up you can generate some <u>serious energy</u>.

Nuclear Fission — *the Splitting Up of Big Atomic Nuclei*

<u>Nuclear power stations</u> generate electricity using <u>nuclear reactors</u>.
In a nuclear reactor, a controlled <u>chain reaction</u> takes place in
which atomic nuclei <u>split up</u> and <u>release energy</u> in the form of <u>heat</u>.
This heat is then simply used to <u>heat water</u> to make steam, which is
used to drive a <u>steam turbine</u> connected to an <u>electricity generator</u>.
The "<u>fuel</u>" that's split is usually <u>uranium-235</u>,
though sometimes it's <u>plutonium-239</u> (or both).

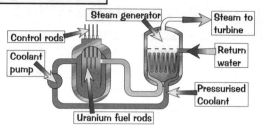

The Chain Reactions:

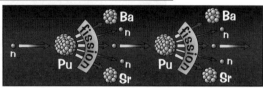 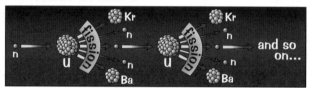

1) For nuclear fission to happen, a <u>slow moving neutron</u> must be <u>absorbed</u> into a uranium or plutonium nucleus. This addition of a neutron makes the nucleus unstable, causing it to <u>split</u>.

2) Each time a <u>uranium</u> or <u>plutonium</u> nucleus <u>splits up</u>, it spits out <u>two or three neutrons</u>, one of which might hit <u>another</u> nucleus, causing it to <u>split</u> also, and thus keeping the <u>chain reaction</u> going.

3) When a large atom splits in two it will form <u>two new smaller nuclei</u>. These new nuclei are usually <u>radioactive</u> because they have the "<u>wrong</u>" number of neutrons in them.

4) A nucleus <u>splitting</u> (called a <u>fission</u>) gives out <u>a lot of energy</u> — lots more energy than you get from any <u>chemical</u> reaction. <u>Nuclear processes</u> release <u>much more energy</u> than chemical processes do. That's why <u>nuclear bombs</u> are <u>so much</u> more <u>powerful</u> than ordinary bombs (which rely on <u>chemical</u> reactions).

5) The <u>main problem</u> with <u>nuclear power</u> is with the disposal of <u>waste</u>. The products left over after nuclear fission are highly <u>radioactive</u>, so they can't just be thrown away. They're very <u>difficult</u> and <u>expensive</u> to dispose of <u>safely</u>.

6) Nuclear <u>fuel</u> is <u>cheap</u> but the <u>overall cost</u> of nuclear power is <u>high</u> due to the cost of the <u>power plant</u> and final <u>decommissioning</u>. Dismantling a nuclear plant safely takes <u>decades</u>.

7) Nuclear power also carries the risk of radiation <u>leaks</u> from the plant or a <u>major catastrophe</u> like <u>Chernobyl</u>.

Nuclear Fusion — *the Joining of Small Atomic Nuclei*

1) Two <u>light nuclei</u> (e.g. hydrogen) can <u>join</u> to create a larger nucleus — this is called <u>nuclear fusion</u>.

2) Fusion releases <u>a lot</u> of energy (<u>more</u> than fission for a given mass) — all the energy released in <u>stars</u> comes from fusion (see next page). So people are trying to develop <u>fusion reactors</u> to generate <u>electricity</u>.

3) Fusion <u>doesn't</u> leave behind a lot of radioactive <u>waste</u> like fission, and there's <u>plenty</u> of hydrogen knocking about to use as <u>fuel</u>.

4) The <u>big problem</u> is that fusion can only happen at <u>really high temperatures</u> — about <u>10 000 000 °C</u>.

5) You can't hold the hydrogen at the <u>high temperatures</u> and <u>pressures</u> required for fusion in an ordinary container — you need an <u>extremely strong magnetic field</u>.

6) There are a few <u>experimental</u> reactors around, but none of them are generating electricity yet. At the moment it takes <u>more power</u> to get up to temperature than the reactor can <u>produce</u>.

Ten million degrees — that's hot...

It'd be great if we could get nuclear fusion to work — there's loads of fuel available and it doesn't create much radioactive waste compared with fission. It's a shame that at the moment we need to use more energy to create the conditions for fusion than we can get out of it. Make sure you know the <u>pros</u> and <u>cons</u> of fission and fusion.

The Life Cycle of Stars

Stars go through <u>many traumatic stages</u> in their lives — just like teenagers.

Protostar

1) Stars <u>initially form</u> from <u>clouds of DUST AND GAS</u>. The <u>force of gravity</u> makes the gas and dust <u>spiral in together</u> to form a <u>protostar</u>.

2) <u>Gravitational energy</u> is converted into <u>heat energy</u>, so the <u>temperature rises</u>. When the temperature gets <u>high enough</u>, <u>hydrogen nuclei</u> undergo <u>nuclear fusion</u> to form <u>helium nuclei</u> and give out massive amounts of <u>heat and light</u>. A star is born. Smaller masses of gas and dust may also pull together to make <u>planets</u> that orbit the star.

Main Sequence Star

3) The star immediately enters a <u>long stable period</u>, where the <u>heat created</u> by the nuclear fusion provides an <u>outward pressure</u> to <u>balance</u> the <u>force of gravity</u> pulling everything <u>inwards</u>. The star maintains its energy output for <u>millions of years</u> due to the <u>massive amounts of hydrogen</u> it consumes. In this <u>stable</u> period it's called a <u>MAIN SEQUENCE STAR</u> and it lasts <u>several billion years</u>. (The Sun is in the middle of this stable period — or to put it another way, the <u>Earth</u> has already had <u>half its innings</u> before the Sun <u>engulfs</u> it!)

Stars much bigger than the Sun   **Stars about the same size as the Sun**

4) Eventually the <u>hydrogen</u> begins to <u>run out</u>. <u>Heavier elements</u> such as iron are made by nuclear fusion of <u>helium</u>. The star then <u>swells</u> into a <u>RED GIANT</u>, if it's a small star, or a <u>RED SUPER GIANT</u> if it's a big star. It becomes <u>red</u> because the surface <u>cools</u>.

Red Giant → **White Dwarf**

Red Super Giant

5) A <u>small-to-medium</u>-sized star like the Sun then becomes unstable and <u>ejects</u> its <u>outer layer</u> of <u>dust and gas</u> as a <u>PLANETARY NEBULA</u>.

6) This leaves behind a hot, dense solid core — a <u>WHITE DWARF</u>, which just cools down to a <u>BLACK DWARF</u> and eventually disappears.

Supernova → **Neutron Star...** → **...or Black Hole**

7) <u>Big stars</u>, however, start to <u>glow brightly again</u> as they undergo more <u>fusion</u> and <u>expand and contract several times</u>, forming elements as <u>heavy as iron</u> in various <u>nuclear reactions</u>. Eventually they explode in a <u>SUPERNOVA</u>, forming elements <u>heavier than iron</u> and ejecting them into the universe to <u>form new planets and stars</u>.

8) The <u>exploding supernova</u> throws the outer layers of <u>dust and gas</u> into space, leaving a <u>very dense core</u> called a <u>NEUTRON STAR</u>. If the star is <u>big enough</u> this will become a <u>BLACK HOLE</u>.

Red Giants, White Dwarfs, Black Holes, Green Ghosts...

The early universe contained <u>only hydrogen</u>, the simplest and lightest element. It's only thanks to <u>nuclear fusion</u> inside stars that we have any of the other <u>naturally occurring elements</u>. Remember — the heaviest element produced in stable stars is iron, but it takes a <u>supernova</u> (or a lab) to create <u>the rest</u>.

Revision Summary for Physics 2b

There's some pretty heavy physics in this section. But just take it one page at a time and it's not so bad.
You're even allowed to go back through the pages for a sneaky peak if you get stuck on these questions.

1)* An AC supply of electricity has a time period of 0.08s. What is its frequency?

2) Name the three wires in a three-core cable.

3) Sketch and label a properly wired three-pin plug.

4) Explain fully how a fuse and earth wire work together.

5) How does an RCCB stop you from getting electrocuted?

6)* Which uses more energy, a 45 W pair of hair straighteners used for 5 minutes, or a 105 W hair dryer used for 2 minutes?

7)* Find the appropriate fuse (3 A, 5 A or 13 A) for these appliances:
a) a toaster rated at 230 V, 1100 W
b) an electric heater rated at 230 V, 2000 W

8)* Calculate the energy transformed by a torch using a 6 V battery when 530 C of charge pass through.

9) Explain how the experiments of Rutherford and Marsden led to the nuclear model of the atom.

10) Draw a table stating the relative mass and charge of the three basic subatomic particles.

11) True or false: radioactive decay can be triggered by certain chemical reactions?

12) What type of subatomic particle is a beta particle?

13) List two places where the level of background radiation is increased and explain why.

14) Name three occupations that have an increased risk of exposure to radiation.

15) Sketch the paths of an alpha particle and a beta particle travelling through an electric field.

16) What is the definition of half-life?

17) Give an example of how gamma radiation can be used in medicine.

18) Which is the most dangerous form of radiation if you eat it? Why?

19) Describe the precautions you should take when handling radioactive sources in the laboratory.

20) Draw a diagram to illustrate the fission of uranium-235 and explain how the chain reaction works.

21) What is the main environmental problem associated with nuclear power?

22) What is nuclear fusion? Why is it difficult to construct a working fusion reactor?

23) Describe the steps that lead to the formation of a main sequence star (like our Sun).

24) Why will our Sun never form a black hole?

*Answers on page 108.

Index

Index

Answers

Revision Summary for Biology 2b (page 38)
28) BB and bb

Example on page 46
A is simple molecular, B is giant metallic,
C is giant covalent, D is giant ionic

Bottom of page 49
1) Cu: 63.5, K: 39, Kr: 84, Cl: 35.5
2) NaOH: 40, Fe_2O_3: 160, C_6H_{14}: 86,
     $Mg(NO_3)_2$: 148

Bottom of page 50
1) a) 30.0% b) 88.9% c) 48.0% d) 65.3%
2) CH_4

Bottom of page 51
1) 21.4 g
2) 38.0 g

Revision Summary for Chemistry 2a (page 54)
9) a) KCl   b) $CaCl_2$
10)

16) A: giant metallic, B: giant covalent,
     C: giant ionic
21) a) 40 b) 108 c) 44 d) 84 e) 106
     f) 81   g) 56   h) 17
23) a)i) 12.0% ii) 27.3% iii) 75.0%
     b)i) 74.2% ii) 70.0% iii) 52.9%
24) $MgSO_4$
25) 80.3 g

Revision Summary for Chemistry 2b (page 69)
3) b)

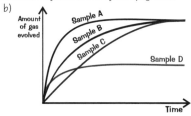

Revision Summary for Physics 2a (page 92)
3) a = (v − u) ÷ t, a = (14 − 0) ÷ 0.4 = 35 m/s²
8) F = ma, a = F ÷ m = 30 ÷ 4 = 7.5 m/s²
9) Downward force of gravity on skydiver:
    F = m × a = 75 × 10 = 750 N.
    Resultant force at 80 mph:
    F = 750 − 650 = 100 N downwards.
    Resultant acceleration:
    a = F ÷ m = 100 ÷ 75 = 1.33 m/s²
10) 120 N
13) Work done = force × distance.
     W = 535 × 12 = 6420 J
14) Ep = m × g × h = 4 × 10 × 30 = 1200 J
15) Ek = ½ × m × v², Ek = ½ × 78 × 23² = 20631 J
16) Ek just as she hits the ground = Ep at the top.
     (g = 10 N/kg),
     So Ek = m × g × h = 78 × 10 × 20 =
     15 600 J
17) Ek transferred = work done by brakes
     ½ × m × v² = F × d
     ½ × 1000 × 2² = 395 × d
     d = 2000 ÷ 395 = 5.1 m
     The car would come to stop in 5.1 m, so no, he
     can't avoid hitting the sheep.

20) P = (m × g × h) ÷ t, (g = 10 N/kg)
     P = (78 × 10 × 20) ÷ 16.5 = 945 W
27) I = Q ÷ t, so I = 240 ÷ (1 × 60) = 4 A
31) V = I × R, so V = 2 × 0.6 = 1.2 V
34) a) Current is the same everywhere in the
     circuit and resistance adds up in a series
     circuit.
     Total resistance = 4 + 6 = 10 Ω
     I = V ÷ R = 12 ÷ 10 = 1.2 A
     b) Potential difference is shared between
     the bulbs.
     V = I × R = 1.2 × 6 = 7.2 V
     c) In parallel, the potential difference is the
     same over each branch of the circuit and is
     equal to the supply potential difference,
     therefore the potential difference over either
     bulb = 12 V.

Revision Summary for Physics 2b (page 106)
1) f = 1 ÷ T, so f = 1 ÷ 0.08 = 12.5 Hz
6) P = E ÷ t, E = P × t
    Hair straighteners: E = 45 × (5 × 60)
    = 13 500 J
    Hair dryer: E = 105 × (2 × 60)
    = 12 600 J
    The hair straighteners use more energy.
7) P = I × V, I = P ÷ V
    a) I = 1100 ÷ 230 = 4.8 A, so use a
    5 A fuse.
    b) I = 2000 ÷ 230 = 8.7 A, so use a
    13 A fuse.
8) E = Q × V
    E = 530 × 6 = 3180 J